CW00337791

The Carpetmakers

The Carpetmakers

Roger Jones
Chris Lakin

McGRAW-HILL Book Company (UK) Limited

London · New York · St Louis · San Francisco · Auckland · Bogotá · Beirut · Düsseldorf · Johannesburg · Lisbon · Lucerne · Madrid · Mexico · Montreal · New Delhi · Panama · Paris · San Juan · São Paulo · Singapore · Sydney · Tokyo · Toronto

Published by
McGraw-Hill Book Company (UK) Limited
Maidenhead · Berkshire · England.

British Library Cataloguing in Publication Data

Jones, Roger
 The carpetmakers.
 1. Management—Case studies
 I. Title   II. Lakin, Chris
 658'.007'22   HD31   78-40656

 ISBN 0−07−084518−2

12345HWV80798

PRINTED AND BOUND IN GREAT BRITAIN

Contents

Senior management at Tufted Carpets

William Birtwhistle,   Director of design
Harold Gammage,   Spinning director
George Gray   Consultant
Howard Johnson,   Business planning and operations executive
Stuart Lennon,   Production director
Jack Leyland,   A second business planning and operations executive

David Markland,   Managing director
John Masterson,   A former managing director
Andrew Muldoon,   Commercial manager
Brian Palmer,   Marketing director
Robert Smith,   Director of home sales
Robin Tenniswood,   Director of production control and purchasing

Prologue

Introducing the chairman

The chairman of Total Furnishing Ltd was an entrepreneur of considerable stature. He had created, almost single-handedly, a sizeable international company from meagre capital resources.

The means by which he had built up Total Furnishings were, in essence, simple. He offered the owners of businesses which were in slow decline or some temporary difficulty, shares and directorships in Total in exchange for their proprietorial rights. Blocks of shares were created for this purpose. Directors tended to retain these shares because they were thought to be a potential source of political power. The fact that only a very small proportion of them were traded on the London Stock Exchange gave directors an additional incentive for retention. The release of one or two blocks would undoubtedly depress their value and so make additional acquisitions expensive. The chairman had exploited their artificially high value to the full.

The chairman himself had few shares in the company and, in theory, he could easily be outvoted by other directors. Such an action by them would, however, appear to be ungrateful, if not disloyal, because they owed both their holdings and their positions largely to his past generosity.

The chairman remained ascendant by virtue of his position and the strength of his personality. His dominance was amply demonstrated at board meetings. On these occasions, none dared interrupt his unending flow of monologue. The other directors played parts akin to those of proverbial Victorian children: they were to be seen and not heard; they were to speak only when spoken to. In the absence of the chairman, the board was incapable of action or decision even on the most minor issues. Directors assumed, quite rightly, that any sign of independent thinking on their part would be seen by the chairman as a challenge to his authority.

The personality of the chairman was flamboyant in the extreme; he was a gifted raconteur and a master of timing. His conversation was salted with the names of the rich, the famous, and the powerful: he gave every impression that he chose his habitual consorts from among these; he was the embodiment of business success. The inferiority felt by the other directors was understandable because he had rescued them from their comparative failure. It was widely assumed in the company that the chairman liked to surround himself with deadwood so as to leave his own freedom of action completely unimpeded. The company was, in fact, a kind of stage on which he could act out his fantasies.

The chairman chose to spend much the greater part of his time abroad. This created problems for him because most of his company's activities were concentrated in Britain. When in London he invariably took a suite at the Dorchester. His main residence was in the Swiss Alps, but he had several other addresses. When in Switzerland he was chauffeur-driven in a blue Rolls-Royce. He undertook his longer journeys in the company's executive jet. It was hard to know just how rich he was personally, but thanks to the company resources which he commanded, he lived opulently. Within the company itself, it was widely rumoured that he was being wooed for even higher things by one of the giant international conglomerates.

The personal qualities which contribute to success in wheeler-dealing are not necessarily assets when it comes to running organizations and factories. The chairman did not know what to do with the companies which he had acquired and incorporated into Total Furnishings. Unlike some other notable entrepreneurs of the takeover age, he did not like the idea of reselling what had just been acquired. His companies represented to him, in a certain psychological sense, bits of real estate. Privately, he felt that he did not yet have enough real estate to put his success and security beyond question.

The chairman was often frustrated by the provincialism and general lack of professional polish among managers in the company's subsidiaries. He tended to attribute shortcomings in production to such defects. In order to remedy these and to provide subsidiaries with some much needed drive and imagination, he created a department of staff experts at head office. The persistent failure of subsidiaries to respond successfully to the stimulation provided by this department served to reinforce his misgivings.

1

A change of captaincy

Masterson's crucifixion

Tufted Carpets was the most important manufacturing subsidiary within the Total Group. It had three factories. Those at Leeds and Cleckheaton each employed about 400. At Batley there was a much smaller establishment employing about 80.

It was acquired by Total in 1968 and since then the chairman had become increasingly dissatisfied with its financial results. In the summer of 1972, he expressed this dissatisfaction by dismissing its managing director. At the time, John Masterson was production director at Tufted and the chairman chose him for the top post. Masterson was a dour Scot who had spent his entire working life in production management within the carpet industry.

Although Masterson did not obtain the immediate and substantial improvement in profits desired by the Chairman, there was little, on the surface, to suggest that he would shortly be following in the footsteps of his predecessor. Certainly none of the other directors and senior managers at Tufted seemed to have the slightest inkling that history would repeat itself within a year.

Masterson, it was true, had had brushes with some of the senior staff at Tufted, but these did not seem to be such as to threaten his own security as managing director. For example, he had been at loggerheads with Andrew Muldoon, the commercial manager. Muldoon was responsible for the accounts department which had been enlarged to accommodate a new system of management accounting introduced recently by a firm of consultants. The chairman considered that this system provided information and controls which could, given technically competent management, do much to enable the company to achieve and sustain a high level of profitability. Masterson resolved to get rid of Muldoon and he offered the job of commercial manager to one of the consultants who had helped to install the accounting system. After some hesitation, the consultant rejected this offer and Muldoon was temporarily reprieved. All this was common knowledge among the resident directors at Tufted, and they imagined that Muldoon's days were strictly numbered.

Masterson's altercations with Stuart Lennon, his successor as production director were perhaps more damaging. Lennon was also a Scot; a tall bronzed athletic man in his mid-forties. In his younger days Lennon had been a professional footballer in the English second division. After retiring from the game, he had worked his way up to the position of production director at a Scottish carpet company before coming south to join Tufted.

The relationship between the two men had, from the start, been difficult. Masterson was reluctant to leave the job of running the factories to Lennon and continued to spend a great deal of time with senior production staff. Indeed, several of these still felt obliged to report directly to Masterson. Eventually, Lennon decided to make a stand, and he requested a private interview with the managing director. Much to his surprise, Lennon found that a senior director from Total was also present at this interview, but Masterson reassured him by explaining that he was free to speak his mind. Lennon complained that he found it very difficult to operate effectively with Masterson always looking over his shoulder. He also indicated that it was his intention to leave the company at the first opportunity.

Early in June 1973, while Masterson was on holiday, Lennon was summoned to a meeting with the chairman at St Albans. Lennon hoped that he had been called to deputize for Masterson, but feared that he was about to be fired. Somewhat to his surprise, he saw that David Markland was also at the meeting. Markland was a corporate planner at Total's head office and, over the past few months, had been visiting Tufted to help with the task of setting budget targets for use in conjunction with the system of management accounting. Neither Markland nor the task on which he had been engaged had excited any particular interest among the directors resident at Tufted. Lennon's perplexity was increased still further by the discussion, which did not have any bearing upon Tufted. He sat silently and diligently through the day's proceedings without becoming any wiser about the reason for his invitation.

In the evening, those still present retired to a bar and Lennon found himself in the company of the deputy chairman and the group finance director. The former said:

'Your contribution to Tufted has been noticed. I would like you to know that we value your services very highly.'

Lennon was reassured by these remarks and assumed that they had heard about his brush with Masterson, but apart from that he hardly knew what else to think.

The following week he, too, went on holiday and his mind was far from the problems at Tufted when he had an urgent telephone call from Brian Palmer, the marketing director. He was told that Masterson had been fired and was replaced by Markland. In a manner that was to be characteristic of his reign, Markland called a crisis meeting of the operating board to take place on the following day. Lennon cursed to himself and reluctantly cut short his holiday.

The new incumbent

David Markland was recruited as a corporate planner by Total in 1972, when he was 31. He came from a military family and was prepared by his earlier education to follow in this tradition. However, shortly after graduating from Sandhurst, he left the army and took up a career in industry. He worked first as a salesman for an electronics company and later became personal assistant to a managing director in another company operating in the same field. He decided that his lack of knowledge of management techniques was a handicap in his new career and he deeply resented his lack of a university degree. He therefore entered a British business school and acquired a degree in business administration. Before joining Total he had worked in the central services department of a large company.

Markland looked every inch an up-and-coming executive. He abounded with confidence and self-assurance; he gave the impression that he was a man of action who could also think. He could talk fluently, with apparent knowledge, about a wide variety of business topics. These dynamic attributes quickly caught the eye of the chairman who saw in Markland some reflection of himself. Like the chairman, Markland managed himself and his financial affairs almost exclusively to impress others. He could be extraordinarily stingy in his relationships with others, although he was extravagant in acquiring property, cars, and other items which symbolize status. He found increasingly that he could give the impression of generosity by entertaining at company expense. These qualities endeared him to the chairman who condescended to advise him on the management of his personal finances.

His rise to favour at Total fed an already intense ambition. He liked to give the impression of being completely self-sufficient and of not needing the help of others. Even those who had known him for years often found it difficult or even impossible to read his moods. In spite of this, he could be vastly entertaining because he was blessed with a ready and sharp wit. He liked to give the impression that everything was a game to him. This, combined with his unusual sense of humour, could make it very difficult to know whether he was joking or serious. The sense of humour, the dynamic exterior, the status expenditures, and the driving ambition made it very hard for him to establish relaxed and easy-going relationships with others.

The chairman could see that Markland had potential as an entrepreneur, but he was impressed most by his apparent mastery of all that was latest in management thinking. He might, the chairman thought, not be able to create an empire, but he looked like a man who would be able to manage one. Already a bright future seemed to be ahead of him at Total Furnishings.

The chairman's patronage

A few days before the demise of Masterson, Markland had been summoned to see the chairman. He was somewhat surprised to find that he was being quizzed about the capabilities of the directors at Tufted.

'What's your opinion of young Palmer?'

Markland was slightly taken aback by the directness of the question and he began to play for time.

'In what respect, chairman?'

'Could he run a company?'

Markland sat silently for a few moments, examining the walls of the office, his face contorted into an expression of deep concentration. Eventually he framed a reply.

'He's quite knowledgeable about the carpet industry, and he's got a lot of contacts with our customers; he's well liked by the staff. . . .'

His voice trailed off and he turned and looked the chairman directly in the eye.

'In my opinion, he's not yet ready for that; he needs to understand far more about the technicalities of management; I think that he could do with a year at business school.'

The chairman was obviously pleased with the answer, he wore a look of satisfaction and nodded with approval at Markland's final assessment. Markland was emboldened by this initial success, and he readily gave opinions of other directors. His answers were all in the same pattern: a few remarks about their qualities and a final assessment that pointed out their shortcomings. He was ready for the final question when it came.

'Could you run one of the group companies?'

'Yes.'

Three days later he was back in Leeds talking with Palmer about the budget that they were due to present to the board meeting in ten minutes time. The telephone rang and it summoned him to the managing director's office to see the chairman. When Markland knocked and entered, the chairman was by the window examining the bleak northern landscape. He turned and faced Markland.

'Mr Masterson has left the company; I am putting you in to take over.'

Markland stood in silence, taking in this surprise announcement. Before he could speak the chairman had begun to outline the terms of the new appointment. There would be a modest increase in salary; a prestigious car; a house provided free of charge for Markland's use while he moved. He was to take over immediately and the remainder of the board would be told straight away.

Almost as an afterthought, the chairman said:

'There is a slight anomaly here that I intend to leave standing. I hired Smith to achieve a break-through in sales, and I had to tempt him away from his previous company. You'll find that his salary is a little higher than your own. We'll put that right next year.'

Neither the chairman nor Markland construed the conversation as being an offer of the job. The chairman was merely moving his players around the chessboard of his company; he did not expect to have to enquire of their opinions except in the most formal of senses. Markland accepted the change in the same manner. It never occurred to him that he might refuse. He had often dreamt of such a moment and had applied himself in a single-minded manner to securing such an appointment. From his conversation with the chairman three days previously, he had hoped for the appointment as managing director of one of the group subsidiaries, but he had not expected to get command of a subsidiary as big or as important as Tufted. For the moment he was so overcome that all he could say was:

'Thank you, Sir.'

The chairman began to ruminate about the company and its prospects.

'I want you to make a million pounds profit next year. You'll get my wholehearted support for all the measures that you deem necessary to achieve this.'

As they moved off to the boardroom, he added quietly:

'It's going to be a make or break year for Tufted.'

2
Early days

Omens

Markland's remit was to revitalize Tufted Carpets so as to establish a firm basis for future profitability. From the external point of view, the omens could have hardly been more propitious. At that time, in the autumn of 1973, the whole of the industrial world was in the grip of a consumer boom of great intensity. If a company like Tufted could not make money at such a time, then it was tempting to say that it would never be able to do so. In fact, company sales and income were reaching record levels. However, within Tufted itself and within Total Furnishings there were a number of hidden problems both operational and political awaiting the new incumbent.

Early affiliations

In the first place, Markland hardly knew anyone at Tufted and this difficulty was compounded by the fact that his position as managing director effectively set him apart from everyone else in the company. However, he had established some kind of contact with both Muldoon and Palmer on his visits to Tufted.

Unlike most of the others at Tufted, Muldoon was able to converse with Markland in the technical language of the new management accounting system. Muldoon felt, quite rightly, that his position was threatened and he did his utmost to impress the visitor from head office. To a large extent Markland succumbed to these blandishments and one of his first acts on becoming managing director was to grant the commercial manager the right to use the boardroom. Markland had this right although the privilege to award the title of 'director' remained solely with the chairman. This elevation of Muldoon did not please the other members of the operating board as he was entirely without friends or support among them.

Markland's commitment to Palmer, the marketing director, also had its origins in the days before he took command of Tufted. Muldoon had gone out of his way to ingratiate himself with Markland in a desperate attempt to secure an ally who might be of use to him in his battle with Masterson. The reasons why Palmer had cultivated the newcomer were rather different. His insecurity was much more internal or psychological, but hardly less real. Among themselves, the other directors at Tufted did not pretend to understand the terminology and the technicalities of the management accounting system. Palmer however spent hour upon hour poring over the accounts in an attempt to understand them and extract meaning. In this way, he hoped to demonstrate outwardly a competence which was entirely lacking. He found Markland responsive to the interest which he showed in the accounts and in the related task of drawing up budgets.

Markland's response had largely been conditioned by the fact that Palmer was the nephew of the deputy chairman and was a substantial shareholder in Total in his own right. He felt that his own interests were being served by the cultivation of this relationship.

Markland knew that Palmer had a purely nominal, but paid directorship, in another company within the group. This provided additional evidence of the marketing director's potential influence. However, there were other reasons of a non-political kind which helped to explain why Markland cultivated a working relationship with Palmer. Above all else he admired the life style of the marketing director and the evident wealth which served to sustain it. Palmer liked to give the impression that he was something of a playboy and this was admired by Markland. The marketing director was still in his twenties and was much the youngest member of the operating board. He was of the same generation as Markland.

The affluence and ease of Palmer's life had helped to breed a certain recklessness which Markland as a member of the 'officer class' much appreciated. This recklessness was particularly demonstrated by his passion for fast driving. The wear and tear on his cars was such that he usually required at least one replacement in the course of a year. In fact, Palmer had been known to get through three company Granadas in such a period.

Early antipathies
Markland took an almost instant dislike to Robert Smith, the director of home sales. This director seemed to have little analytical understanding of management; he seemed to be guided solely by experience and instinct. Markland found his indifference towards paperwork intensely annoying. This antipathy was increased further by his knowledge that Smith received a higher salary than himself. The last year or two had been something of an education to Markland in the finer points of expense account living, but the magnitude of Smith's expenses came as a revelation to him. It rankled him that he was

expected to sign these without protest. He considered all this but knew inwardly that his dislike of Smith had deeper roots which he could not as yet explain. However, he knew that Smith enjoyed a high reputation throughout Total as a super salesman. Indeed, it was widely thought that his efforts had in the past saved Tufted from the worst. It seemed that Smith's position was, for the moment at least, impregnable.

Markland held Lennon in contempt. This director seemed to lack even the faintest appreciation of management accounting and other prerequisites of modern management. However, such disabilities were not unique to Lennon. It may have been that Markland resented Lennon's fine physique and felt a need to dominate or humiliate him by psychological means. Although Lennon's full head of hair was grey, he nevertheless looked younger than Markland even though he was at least fifteen years his senior. Lennon, who had been a professional footballer, continued to take a keen and informed interest in this diversion. Markland had an almost irrational hatred of the game. In his mind that settled the issue: Lennon would have to go.

Markland thought that Robin Tenniswood, the director of production control and purchasing, was a fussy old woman. Certainly, Tenniswood was quietly spoken and highly respectable. In his leisure time he was a keen organizer of church bazaars and fêtes. He was an avid reader of both the *Daily Telegraph* and trade journals. The other directors did little more than glance at newspapers and periodicals; they preferred to obtain most of their general knowledge of economic and political affairs from watching television.

Markland believed that the deficiencies of these two directors were readily demonstrable and he decided to approach the chairman in order to obtain their removal. Action of this kind, he believed, would do much to firmly establish his dominance over the operating board.

Export and transfer prices
Markland quickly appreciated that Tufted was charging very low prices for the carpets which it exported to Europe. He saw that a moderate increase here would do much to improve Tufted's financial position. He also realized that Tufted tended to under-charge for the carpet which it supplied to other subsidiaries within the Total Group at home. It seemed to him to be slightly unfair to blame Tufted for poor financial results when it was on the receiving end of transfer pricing. He appreciated also that he would have to proceed with much caution on both issues and most especially on the former.

The group export sales director also had a seat on the board at

Tufted. This director happened to head a private trading company which had its headquarters in a large country house near St Albans. This company dealt in carpets, and in particular, it was the selling agent for third party overseas sales of carpets produced by Total Furnishings. By virtue of his directorship on the main board of Total and various subsidiaries he also controlled exports to the overseas outlets of Total Furnishings. His status in the boardroom at Tufted was confirmed by his close contacts with the chairman who, incidentally, had had in the past a formal connection with the trading company. The status of the export sales director was reaffirmed by the fact that he invariably arrived for board meetings at Tufted in a chauffeur-driven Rolls-Royce. The chairman usually arrived in a relatively humble Rover 3500 as he preferred to keep his best limousine in his country of domicile, in the Alps.

Markland knew that he had to approach the question of export prices with extreme caution, but he felt it might be possible to suggest privately to the chairman that export prices could be increased modestly.

The origins of a policy

The management accounts provided Markland with his principal source of information about operations at Tufted. He believed that this information provided a basis for making policy decisions even though he sometimes found the data and terminology of these accounts hard to understand.

The sales section of the accounts listed fifty-three separate kinds of carpet. He could recognize some of these from their names, but did not know what most of them looked like. His study of the accounts revealed an unmistakable pattern. They seemed to show incontrovertibly that large quantities of carpet were being sold at a loss in the lower end of the market. It also seemed clear from the accounts that several of the more luxurious kinds of carpets were being sold, admittedly in much smaller amounts, at a profit. Markland calculated that modest increases in the price of the cheaper carpets would generally convert many losses into profits. He also came to the conclusion that the sales of the profit-making lines could be increased if their prices were reduced slightly. These reductions would, he calculated, still leave a margin to spare. The idea seemed so obvious and attractive that he found it hard to understand why nobody had thought of it before.

At the time, neither he nor anyone else knew that the estimated production costs embodied in the management accounts seriously misrepresented actual costs. In general, the costs of production on

19

the allegedly loss-making carpets were overestimated. The reverse applied to most of the so-called profit makers.

Markland presented the outlines of his new price policy to the operating board, and he was gratified by the enthusiasm with which it was received by the directors. Muldoon, however, was obliged to list the difficulties involved in implementing this policy. There were, he pointed out, several price lists in existence and each reflected the varying discounts given to different sorts of customer. The revision of these lists and their reprinting would, he contended, involve much work and take several weeks to accomplish. He also reminded Markland that it would be necessary to differentiate between orders received before, and those after, price increases. Among other things, he pointed out, this would mean changing the computer program in respect of invoices. The whole administration was, he asserted, designed on the basis that prices would only be considered at six-monthly intervals and would in the meantime remain unchanged. In order to implement the proposed price changes it would be necessary to reschedule the activities of his department in order to accommodate the extra work involved. At no time did Muldoon indicate an unwillingness to do this. He was simply making the point that there would be much inevitable delay in the implementation of the proposed price changes.

There were further problems which Muldoon went on to describe. He pointed out that prices could not be increased without the approval of the Price Commission. Prices, he indicated, could only be increased if they reflected increases in costs. He would have to prepare a submission on this basis and this would involve weeks of work and delay. Finally, the delay could be very protracted if the Commission rejected the initial application. Markland was dismayed by the administrative problems which simple price changes seemed to create. These difficulties suggested the thought in Markland's mind that it might be a good idea to concentrate effort both in production and sales on the more expensive ranges of carpet. However, he remained convinced that the faulty price structure at Tufted was the major reason why the company had not returned profits of the kind which the chairman would have liked. It was obvious to him that the implementation of a sensible price policy would require much planning. He therefore resolved to appoint three product managers to help with this task. Each of these would be responsible for a particular segment of the carpet market. Each would monitor the sales of particular categories of carpet and would help to decide what price changes were required. Palmer received this suggestion with some enthusiasm. He welcomed additions to his rather small department, and the recruitment was put into motion. Eventually two appointments were made, one by internal transfer and the other by the recruitment of someone from outside. The third position was never filled.

3
The recruitment of executives

Markland approaches the chairman
The chairman listened to Markland's strictures on the deficiencies of Lennon and Tenniswood attentively and with apparent sympathy. He was, as usual, much impressed by the clarity and forcefulness of the managing director's arguments. However, he advised a certain caution in respect of tactics.

'I don't really like getting rid of directors before we are in a position to replace them. It can leave you with an awkward gap.'

Markland did not oppose this view, and after a momentary pause the chairman continued:

'If I were you, I'd get a couple of up-and-coming executives into the company, and if they turn out well, we could easily make room for them on the board.'

These remarks had an air of finality about them and Markland did not quite have the conviction to press his opinions further. Characteristically, he acted on the advice without hesitation. Within seconds of the chairman's departure, he started to make arrangements for advertisements to be placed in *The Times*, *The Guardian*, and *The Financial Times*.

Howard Johnson's recruitment
Over fifty replies were received for the advertised post of 'business planning and operations executive'. One of these was from Howard Johnson. He, like Markland, was in his early thirties. He had graduated from university as an engineer and then obtained employment in that capacity in a large electrical company. He found this work very dull, and he obtained a transfer to a department of management science. After four years in this company he left to take up an appointment in a highly reputable firm of management consultants. He remained in this new employment for a further five years, but by then had become tired of living out of suitcases and of drawing endless flow charts. His next job was as general manager and director of a small manufacturing firm in the East Midlands. In spite of its impressive title, he found that this job did not extend him in any way.

Such scope as the job might have had was removed by the owner of the business who interested himself, not only in the deployment of company funds, but also in the minutiae of day-to-day routine.

Johnson's letter in response to the Tufted advertisement was posted mechanically. At the time it had no more significance to him than countless others which he had sent. The initial exchanges of acknowledgements, the form of application, and the subsequent interview invitation hardly filled him with enthusiasm. His image of the company was already unfavourable. He disliked the shade of blue which was used to head the company's notepaper. He was offended by the stern command printed at the foot of the page: 'Address all correspondence to the company and not to individuals'. By this time he was something of a connoisseur in the design of application forms. The one sent by Tufted Carpets affronted him aesthetically. What was even worse, it also insulted his common sense. The pre-printed headings on the form asked for information about a curious miscellany. These requests were supplemented by further typed demands to disclose: 'What position do you expect to occupy in five years' time?'; 'In ten years' time?'; 'What is your greatest ambition?' By now he had become used to such questions and dutifully wrote: 'managing director of Tufted Carpets Ltd'; 'group managing director'; and 'To make a significant contribution to British industry'. He was perplexed by the mixture of old and new in the application form. It was as if the printed part had been issued in the last century, only to be rediscovered by the company archivist who, for the sake of economy, decided it would be a pity to waste it. The typed section looked as though it had been copied straight out of a next year's issue of *Management Today*. He was not to know at this stage that the boardroom at Tufted itself had, since Markland's arrival, become a mixture of the antiquated and the ultra-modern.

He later received an acknowledgement thanking him for his application for the post of 'product manager'. In the next post he received a further communication apologizing for this error and thanking him for his application for the position of 'business planning and operations executive'. Finally, an invitation came for him to attend an interview to held in an hotel near the motorway south of Leeds.

During his career as a management consultant he had spent a year at one of the large multiple tailoring companies. He then took the opportunity of buying several suits. By 1973, however, the styles of 1968 looked rather dated. Narrow lapels and tapered trouser legs were no longer in vogue. His recent excursion into the fashion trade had resulted in his purchase of a suit that contrasted sharply with his existing wardrobe. He had not yet worn this new aberration to work, and he intended to spend the morning of the interview day at the office. In order to save himself from embarrassment he changed into his new attire in a gents at one of the service stations on the way to Leeds. The largeness of the lapels and the rather bell bottomed trousers gave him, he thought, a faintly nautical look.

After a short wait in the hotel, he was summoned to the interview room. The door was swept open by a man whose premature baldness made him appear older than he was. He shook Johnson firmly by the hand—smiled—and succinctly introduced himself.

'Markland.'

Johnson was immediately impressed, and became more so as the interview progressed. Markland reminded him of certain highly successful consultants he had known. He had the unmistakable impression that he was being interviewed by a man of action who seemed to generate vitality. The misgivings which he had felt about Tufted were by the end of the interview, almost entirely dispelled.

There was in his mind some confusion as to what was actually involved in the job of 'business planning and operations executive'. Markland attempted to resolve this by explaining the organizational weaknesses which he saw at Tufted. Johnson was impressed by the grasp of detail and the analytic skill which Markland demonstrated in the course of this explanation. Even so, he was still not absolutely clear about the precise definition of the job in question, but he had the distinct impression that the position was really that of an assistant to the managing director. He felt quite enthusiastic at the prospect of working closely with a man of Markland's evident talent.

A few days later Markland telephoned and invited him to a further interview to be held in the main factory at Leeds. The interview was scheduled for the following Thursday, 4 October, and would, Markland said, take the whole of the afternoon. At this second interview, Johnson's favourable opinion of Markland was reinforced. The latter introduced him to Palmer and Lennon who, he said, would be interviewing him later. Johnson found his interview with these two directors somewhat deflating; they had none of Markland's ebullience and they conducted the interview in a disinterested way.

However, his enthusiasm was quickly restored by a brisk tour of the factory with the managing director. The factory itself seemed to have an air of quiet efficiency. For the most part, it was a single storey structure. Its most impressive architectural feature was a huge warehouse which reminded Johnson of a film set he had seen in a James Bond epic. The racking for rolls of broadloom carpet soared fifty feet into the air. Carpet was handled by five cranes which moved vertically and horizontally along separate gangways. Markland said:

'Impressive, don't you think? It holds over 1000 broadloom rolls. That's enough to carpet 200 acres. I've calculated that laid end to end it would stretch for fifty miles.'

Afterwards, in the managing director's office, they refreshed themselves with a tray of tea. Quite suddenly, after some general observations Markland said:

'Will you join us then?'

He outlined the company's terms—salary, car, holidays, moving expenses, and pension scheme. The company was going to be particularly generous about removal expenses. Among other things, Markland offered him a company house rent free for up to six months. Johnson was a little concerned that the job was subject to only one month's notice. Markland brushed this doubt aside by indicating that this was group policy and, therefore, beyond his power to alter. Rather foolishly, Johnson accepted this without further question.

Normally, offers of this kind are first stated in writing, and in these circumstances applicants can consider terms leisurely and dispassionately. The verbal proposal coming at the end of an exhausting and stressful afternoon had caught Johnson with his guard down. He felt grateful to Markland for the offer, and given his earlier expenditure of emotional energy it was hardly surprising that he did not bargain vigorously to secure better terms.

Jack Leyland's recruitment

Jack Leyland was a few years younger than Johnson. He had degrees in both chemistry and statistics. After leaving university he worked for one, and then another, large company. In both, he performed the duties of an internal consultant.

In some ways Johnson's personality mirrored Markland's. Leyland, however, presented a contrast to both. He was phlegmatic and lacked their ebullience. He gave the impression, without any conscious effort on his part, that he was above all else systematic and immensely hard working. His dourness gave the impression of an almost Germanic solidity and thoroughness. Markland believed that Johnson was, like himself, first and foremost an ideas man. Leyland, he thought, looked like the man they both needed to do the backroom work.

Leyland looked the part as did the other two, but he dressed without a trace of their flashiness. Markland saw beneath this sober exterior, and he sensed that Leyland had ambitions which were almost as consuming as his own. He looked like the ideal man to add some balance, if not ballast to his management team. In spite of the acuity of some of his perceptions, Markland did not penetrate all that far beneath the public face which Leyland presented. In truth, Leyland did not have all the persistence which his image promised. Nor was he nearly as hard. In fact, behind the sober exterior, he was warm and very human. The real man could be glimpsed when he laughed. At such times, he often showed an almost child-like innocence and capacity for enjoying simple things. There had been little cause for spontaneous laughter in his interviews with Markland.

Leyland had become intensely bored and frustrated by his work as an internal consultant. He had churned out one report after another which were not even read, let alone acted upon. On his bad days, he felt really depressed at the thought of the dust which was gathering on these tomes. He had decided on a career in industry as opposed to one at university because he wanted to do things rather than think about them. His present situation seemed to him to be especially ironic. More out of frustration than positive belief, he had for a while been trying to get himself a job in line management so as to be nearer some action. He replied to the same advertisement as Johnson, not because it seemed to promise what he really wanted, but because he lived nearby at Skipton. There was, he thought, nothing to lose.

He too was impressed by Markland for much the same reasons as Johnson, but he also was uncertain about what the job of 'business planning and operations executive' entailed. He established that he would report directly to Markland himself, but the job did not seem to him to be like that of a personal assistant to the managing director. The latter had described to him the weaknesses which he saw at Tufted especially in relation to areas like stock and production control. He understood that he would assist in the task of analysing these weaknesses. After this preliminary work was completed, he had the impression that the managing director would, at the first opportunity, transfer him to a line position of significant responsibility.

He accepted similar terms to Johnson except that his salary was rather lower, and in his case a company car was not included.

Markland's subsequent letters

Johnson was due to take up his appointment at the beginning of November, and Leyland a week or two later. Sometime after they had handed in their notices to their employers, both men were disturbed and disconcerted by subsequent letters which they received from Markland.

Johnson, in fact, received his no more than a week before he was due to take up his new appointment. He had firmly understood that the advertisement for a 'business planning and operations executive' applied to a single vacancy. The letter told him that there would be a second appointee with the same title. This blow was softened a little by some further disclosures. He was informed that his appointment was much the senior of the two. The letter concluded with a brief outline of Leyland's career to date.

Leyland received a similar letter at about the same time. He too had been under the impression that he was the sole appointee. The letter suggested that the second appointment would be only slightly senior to his own. He was informed that this senior appointee would be concerned with rather different aspects of the business than he would. The letter concluded with a brief description of Johnson's career and credentials.

Their respective letters made both men feel insecure. Johnson might have a rival; Leyland had effectively been demoted before he had even started. The enthusiasm that both men had felt at the prospect of their new jobs was now tinged with a vague apprehension.

4
Dilemma

Scapegoats and inflexibilities

The financial year for Total Furnishings ended on the thirtieth of June. In the month or two which followed the shape of the financial accounts for the group and its subsidiaries gradually became clearer. These were anxious times at Tufted. The chairman's dissatisfaction with profits had been the main cause of Masterson's departure. This managing director was not the first victim to be sacrificed to assuage the chairman's wrath. It remained to be seen if he would be the last.

The mid-summer period was known among the staff at Tufted's as 'the chairman's silly season'. Year after year they did things which most of them knew were futile and even damaging. At such times the boardroom and the directors' offices witnessed scenes of frenetic activity and near panic as last ditch efforts were made to accomplish things which put a more favourable gloss on the accounts. For instance, regardless of the state of orders great exertions were made to maximize production. This was done in order to increase the value of stocks and work-in-progress. Production managers would make sure that more or less any of the raw material at hand was converted into broadloom carpet. It even happened that large quantities of various kinds of carpet were produced which had long since been withdrawn from the catalogue. Contrary to the lessons of experience, it was hoped that this output would fill the shortfall in production caused by the summer holidays. The flaw in this expectation was that many potential customers were also on holiday and were spending their money on things other than carpets.

Subsequently, much of this extra output had to be sold at knock down prices. The effort to create the illusion of profit on paper thus had the absurdly paradoxical result of stimulating the production of loss-making carpet. Less obviously, this expedient was one of several factors which served to undermine co-ordination between production, sales and purchasing.

The search for a magical solution in the form of a new design or type of carpet went on more or less continuously. Against all past experience it was hoped that a product innovation would lay the foundation for commercial success. The catalogue grew larger and larger with the passage of time. This process generated jobs and with them vested interests and entrenched attitudes. The idea that the company should concentrate its effort on a more limited range, which was relatively easy to make and sell, had become unacceptable.

Such was Markland's inheritance. He might have come to appreciate it earlier had he been surrounded by outspoken men who put truth before self-interest. Instead, he was enveloped in a web of ingratiation and misrepresentation.

A self-contained world

It would be wrong to think that Markland had anything like a full appreciation, either instinctively or intellectually, of the social and operational isolation which engulfed him. Indeed, for the first time in his life, he was surrounded by people who wished to please him. This circumstance combined with the elation he felt at his rapid rise to favour made him less, rather than more, sensitive to the fact of isolation. His perception was made less acute by this intoxicating success. Within Tufted, at least, he felt little obligation to return considerateness. In fact, he greatly enjoyed insulting those who grovelled before him.

The isolation which encompassed him was cultural and psychological, but it was compounded by physical restrictions. His office was the most inaccessible and private room in the building. It was part of a three-roomed suite which also contained his personal secretary's office and the boardroom. Prospective visitors had first to negotiate their way past a receptionist in the foyer which led to a reserved car park. Afterwards they were obliged to obtain a further clearance from his personal secretary.

The suite of rooms was on one side of an L-shaped corridor. It was impossible to see into it from this passage and its doors carried 'Strictly Private' signs. The privacy of the managing director's and his secretary's offices were further enhanced by the fact that their external walls abutted upon farm land. These rooms enjoyed a semi-rural view of distant hills, and here one was as far away as possible, given the circumstances, from the grime of industry.

The L-shaped passage continued on the far side of the foyer. This entrance area contrived to give a visitor the impression that he was entering a civilized and urbane place. It was furnished with easy chairs and plush carpet, and was adorned with potted plants and artistic prints. The latter suggested a degree of culture which was, in fact, entirely absent.

Some directors and managers had offices along this further section of corridor. These rooms had, relatively speaking, less privacy: they had both internal and external windows and looked out onto the reserved parking area. However, a certain discreetness was preserved by the use of net curtains.

The corridor led to staff departments which, incidentally, served to insulate the directors' quarters completely from the cruder environment of the factory itself. Only two doors led from these departments to the shop floor. Both carried the stern command:

'Operatives NOT admitted without authorization.'

This marked a frontier which was seldom breached from either side.

Boardroom conventions

The boardroom and the suite to which it belonged were carpeted with the most lavish of the company's products. Chairs were arranged along a long mahogany table. The room opened slightly at one end, where bay windows looked out onto flowerbeds and the edge of the reserved parking area. This alcove contained a desk and chair. The latter was much more ostentatious than others in the room. It was occupied by Markland during formal board meetings except on those occasions when the chairman was present. The only other piece of furniture of note was a drinks cabinet conveniently placed beside the large chair. A picture of the Queen adorned the wall opposite. This was made of woven silk and it had been presented by a visiting Japanese businessman.

In this room the directors habitually took their morning coffee and afternoon tea as well as lunch. Lennon and the director of design, William Birtwhistle, more often than not visited it on all these occasions even though their personal offices were located at the mill in Cleckheaton.

The difference between the managing director at Tufted and the other resident directors was one of kind rather than degree. There were, it was true, differences of weight among resident directors. Probably, Smith was the most influential on account of his seniority, his undeniable reputation as a first class salesman, and his high salary. Palmer had more weight than one might at first expect, because of both his substantial shareholding and his family connections within the Total Group. Comparative newcomers like Birtwhistle and Harold Gammage, the spinning director, lacked advantages of this kind. Consequently, little weight tended to be attached to their opinions. They did not, for this good reason, choose to express these at formal board meetings; they were well aware that their main, if not only, function on these occasions was to help make a respectable quorum.

Differences of weight did not prevent the resident directors from regarding each other as social equals. This equality was confirmed by the ribald chit-chat which was common among them. Again, it was symbolized by the fact that they sat lengthwise along the boardroom table where it was convenient, rather than where seniority might prescribe. There was only one slight exception to this. In the absence of the managing director, Palmer would sit at the head of the table if it happened to be empty. If by chance someone had already occupied it he would not, as Markland did, claim it for himself.

Most importantly, equality among the resident directors was preserved by a deeply established and many sided convention. It was accepted that a director could fight to maintain the boundaries of his department and his sovereignty over his territory. Directors were constrained by this convention from interfering in the affairs of departments for which they were not responsible. A managing director was obliged to deal with a department entirely through the director or manager responsible for it. Masterson had displeased his masters because he had, in his relations with Lennon, defied this taboo. A managing director could seek to adjust the boundaries between departments, but he was obliged to respect them so long as they remained intact. The adjustment of boundaries by a managing director was a task which demanded the utmost tact and the observance of much protocol. Certain territories were so well established that it would be easier for him to dismiss those who presided over them than it would be for him to change their respective boundaries.

The convention governing demarcation and the rights of departmental heads was well understood by members of the board; they were, in fact, its guardians. Even so few, if any, of them would have been able to describe the convention accurately and comprehensively; it was something they felt rather than articulated. The convention survived changes in the composition of the boardroom and, at the same time, it grew in its ramifications and subtlety.

One of the most important consequences of the convention was that it effectively cut off a managing director from most of those below the rank of director. The main exceptions to this were people like chauffeurs, secretaries, cleaners, and tea ladies. These performed roles similar to those of servants in private households, and they tended to exhibit the servility characteristics of that category. A managing director's contact with this sort of person would not give him a representative picture of those who worked in production and maintenance departments. The directors themselves could scarcely be described as servile. It would be more accurate to call them deferential; they were masters of the higher rather than the lower forms of ingratiation.

Their behaviour towards Markland in the boardroom provided regular demonstrations of this mastery. They acquiesced without protest in certain changes which he imposed upon the ritualistic side of board-room life. For instance, Masterson had left the drinks cabinet open at all times and the directors could help themselves when, and as often, as they liked. Markland imposed an almost complete temperance on the boardroom. He locked the drinks cabinet and kept the key on his person. The cabinet was kept open only when the chairman visited the premises. Sometimes, late in the evening after a particularly exhausting meeting, Markland would relax the austerity and serve drinks. This relaxation of custom was due more to his own pressing need than to any consideration for others.

Markland symbolized the new regime of sobriety by drinking a pint of milk with his lunch in the boardroom. Palmer was quick to follow this example, but this degree of self-abasement was altogether too much for the other directors. In the absence of Markland, no one was the predetermined centre of attention. As soon as he entered the room he became the focus of conversation. Normally, football and the television programmes of the previous night constituted the favourite subjects of boardroom conversation. These topics were highly distasteful to Markland. The directors showed their mastery of in-gratiation by taking up his conversational cues with alacrity. Mostly, he imposed on his audience a topic relevant either to Tufted or to busi-ness life in general. When the boardroom was full, discreet conversa-tions not involving Markland were possible. However, in these circumstances he could, by raising his voice, instantly re-establish conversational monopoly.

The directors were adept at responding to Markland's apparent moods. They gave the impression that his jokes were funnier than their own. If he looked tired or unwell they would invariably express their concern. He could be rude to them, but the rules of the game forbade them to retaliate in kind. They applauded him when they considered he was right, and did just the same when they thought he was mistaken. He became enveloped by the blanket of ingratiation which they wove around him: it cut him off from reality; it made it difficult, if not impossible, for him to distinguish truth from falsehood.

Practically all the sections of Tufted Carpets came under the juris-diction of one or other of the resident directors. They told Markland as little, or as much, as they thought it was desirable for him to know about these sections. The only important exceptions to these arrange-ments were the accounts and data processing sections presided over by Muldoon, and the management services section which was headed by a manager who reported directly to Markland. This manager was, because of his relative lack of status, even more cautious in his dealings with him than were the resident directors. Markland did not have any obvious ways to check the veracity of what subordinates told him. He could ask for specific information, and request or order that certain things be done within a section or department, but his conception of that department was limited by the censored information which reached him. Nor was there any guarantee that his wishes would be acted upon in the absence of close surveillance. Departmental heads could be very resourceful in their calculated obstruction and inefficiency. Markland did, on paper, possess Draconian powers to ensure compliance with his wishes. He did have, for instance, the formal power to dismiss resident directors although this did require the approval of the chairman. However, even in respect of the managers who reported directly to him, his power was not such that it was possible for him to act without making it seem as though the punishment fitted the crime.

He more than half believed that the newly installed management accounting system, in conjunction with the budget targets which he had helped to draw up, gave him the necessary instrument of information and control. His belief in the efficacy of such systems was one of the more important by-products of his business education. The system of management accounting itself was beyond the comprehension of the resident directors, and the budgets appeared to them to have no real connection with day-to-day activities. They chose therefore to ignore the system rather than to manipulate it. Quite rightly, they perceived his chosen instrument of control as an irrelevance. The management accounting system with its attendant budgets was not seen as a threat to the demarcations of their departments or to their sovereignty. The connection between the activities of the accounts department and the rest of the organization was at best tenuous. Consequently, the growth in the size and complexity of this department did not impinge on others in any politically important way. The masses of information which this department produced helped to sustain the fantasy in Markland's mind that he was at the apex of an information system. The other half of this fantasy was that he made, or could make, decisions on the basis of this information.

Within Tufted Carpets, his isolation was social as well as operational. Social equals signal to each other disapproval as well as approval. To some extent too they can drop the mask of disguise and reveal something of their real selves. Limited disclosures of this kind and the responses which they engender help to keep a person in touch with his own limitations. Markland felt, quite rightly, that disclosures of this kind were incompatible with the position he now held. If, by chance he made a disclosure, his audience would appear not to notice it or react in some other artificial way. The members of the boardroom attempted to adapt themselves to his moods; he never felt obliged to adapt his posture to theirs. In the absence of the negative signals that are normal in human intercourse, a chief executive can easily become the victim of his own private delusions of grandeur.

Markland's habitual consorts—the resident directors—were usually able to sustain the mask of deference, even under trying circumstances. Indeed, their success in life could largely be attributed to this capacity. Generally speaking, those in more subordinate positions are more limited in this capacity. The workers on the shop floor, for instance, had some curiosity concerning their new governor, but they were, nevertheless, relieved that his inspection tours were conducted briskly. Had he chosen to stay for any length of time on the shop floor, there would have been much uncertainty about how he and they should comport themselves. The pressures to avoid contact with social inferiors except under certain well regulated circumstances were also felt strongly by other directors. Even Lennon, who was responsible for production, spent surprisingly little time on the shop floor. He showed more of the common touch than any of the other resident directors with the possible exception of Gammage. Lennon could maintain his distance while adopting an easy intimacy in his conversation. He was able to drop this cordiality instantly to correct a workman with harsh abruptness. Lennon observed protocol and attempted to maintain contact with the shop floor primarily through production managers and supervisors. Like all the resident directors he found the company of social equals the least stressful. He, in common with other resident directors, did not find the company of senior directors from Total, or, for that matter, contact with Markland, particularly relaxing. However, these upward relations had to be cultivated in the interests of survival, if not advancement.

The resident directors themselves suffered, admittedly in a less intense form, from the same kind of isolation which afflicted Markland. For instance, Tenniswood, Smith, and Palmer might not even set foot in any of the three factories for months on end. Their isolation made it even more difficult for Markland to catch a glimpse of the reality outside the boardroom itself and the flow of paper issuing from the accounts department. One reason why the resident directors were singularly uninformative about what went on at Tufted was that they were so limited in their own knowledge of this.

The fact of isolation—both in the operational and the social senses—was the chief element in Markland's predicament. How could he hope to pierce this barrier in order to exert some directional influence over the company which he ostensibly headed? There was little, if any evidence to suggest that in his early days he had any real appreciation of this problem. At business school, isolation was not a topic which was discussed. He had played at being a director with other students in case study discussions, in role playing exercises, and in management games. But these activities assumed a degree of omnipotence and control on the part of directors and managing directors which is not mirrored in the world of business itself. Markland therefore lacked the intellectual equipment to appreciate, let alone manage, the central fact of existence at Tufted Carpets—isolation.

He was also lacking in relevant general experience. With the possible exception of Palmer, he was in comparison to the resident directors a relative newcomer to the industry. This, undoubtedly, made it more difficult for him to adapt to his new circumstances.

If he had worked his way through the ranks of management at Tufted to the top position he would have acquired some understanding of the inner workings of that company on the way. For instance, he would have had many opportunities to observe particular individuals in circumstances where they dropped the mask of deference. Again, he would have learned something at least about who talks to whom. It is possible that he might even have learned something about the production and maintenance departments which were physically separate from the office accommodation. Knowledge of this kind was automatically denied to him as the new incumbent coming in from the outside.

Admittedly he had established some rapport with Muldoon and Palmer when he had visited Tufted in connection with his work on budgets. At that time Muldoon was under a cloud, and he had, in any case, never been a member of a significant grapevine. Palmer was, on paper, a weightier ally, but he lacked confidence in his own abilities. He tried to hide this by adopting defensive attitudes and by standing on his dignity a great deal. These two could take a lot, but were incapable of giving much in return. Contact with them hardly made up for Markland's lack of prior knowledge about Tufted Carpets.

However, the experience gained by working one's way up the ranks carries with it special problems. For instance, those who in the past supported the person promoted to the top position will now look to him for recompense. The new incumbent will, in these circumstances, have the delicate task of freeing himself from at least some of these obligations while retaining the services of reliable informants. Again, the experience acquired by progressing through the ranks is itself a wasting asset. However, for a time it has its uses. Markland did, at least, have the advantage of freedom from the pressures which former colleagues are apt to exert.

Setting the pattern for future events

Markland's reaction to the isolation imposed upon him by his appointment was partly conditioned by the kind of man he was and partly by his experience. These two elements were interwoven because his career to date reflected the choices which he had made. Outwardly, or in the active sense, the chairman had selected him to be managing director of Tufted Carpets, but Markland had sought such promotion and, when it was offered, accepted it readily. In this sense he had chosen to become what he now was—managing director of Tufted Carpets.

His experience at the military academy and in the army itself had had a deep influence on his character and how he responded to others. This was hardly surprising in view of his family traditions. One legacy of this influence was that he had acquired the habit of barking at people. As soon as he arrived as managing director he started to make warlike noises.

Before his appointment senior staff came and went more or less at their own discretion. Markland at once instituted a system of time checks in respect of these staff. This, he called, 'the a.m. arrivals list'. All senior staff with the single exception of himself were entered on this if they arrived after 8.45 a.m. After this time the list was broken down into five minute periods and gatemen entered the names of latecomers in appropriate segments. In small ways this system changed the habits of resident directors. For example, Lennon had been in the habit of calling at the Leeds factory early in the morning before going on later to Cleckheaton. After the introduction of the checking procedure, he reversed the procedure in order to escape its clutches. Muldoon passed Cleckheaton on his journey to work at the Leeds factory. Before the imposition of the new procedure he had, but rarely, set foot on the Cleckheaton premises. Now, whenever he was late, he seemed to find some reason or other for stopping off at Cleckheaton. Other directors did not go to these extremes but they would exchange knowing winks with gatemen who as a result made minor, but favourable, adjustments to their recorded times of arrival.

Shortly after the introduction of this procedure Markland underlined its importance by circulating copies of the list to the resident directors and other senior staff. Even Tenniswood was driven to voice some muted criticism of this additional refinement. It was abrasively brushed aside with the remark:

'It's up to you to set an example to your juniors in punctuality. How can we hope to discipline them for slacking if they see you coming in without any regard for the proper starting time.'

Later, shortly after taking up his appointment as business planning and operations executive, Johnson also had the temerity to query the procedure:

'I feel it's a bad thing. Are you buying my ability or my time?'

Markland replied in a typical vein:

'I don't know yet what your ability is, so meanwhile I'll settle for your time.'

The military influence was also affirmed by his habit of sending individuals written reprimands even for minor infractions. Again, it was exemplified by his habit of making inspection tours of the factories accompanied by an entourage of junior officers. These were, characteristically, conducted at breakneck speed so that some of the more overweight members of the entourage found it as much as they could do to maintain even a trailing position behind their leader.

This military style was also demonstrated by the method he chose to handle industrial relations. After walk-outs and other forms of action he would call workers together to address them *en masse*. Their discontent, he imagined, would be allayed by morale boosting activity of this kind.

Astonishingly, he seemed to believe that his orders would be automatically obeyed. In spite of abundant evidence to the contrary, he never really abandoned this expectation. For instance, he once instructed Palmer in the following tones:

'Sack that man with the curly pipe who hangs about these corridors with nothing to do.'

A month or so later he was heard to shout at Palmer:

'I thought I told you to sack that man with the curly pipe. He used to live at the front of the building. I now see he appears at the back. For God's sake get rid of him.'

Palmer did so by transferring him to the mill at Cleckheaton.

Markland had come to more than half believe that his words both written and spoken were synonymous with action. This delusion was the result mainly of the combined effects of his self-absorption and the isolation which encompassed him. An incident which he himself related to Leyland, shortly after the latter came to Tufted, serves to illustrate how words and action had become confused in his mind. Lennon came to Markland to ask for advice about how he should respond to the pay demands which the assistant dyehouse manager and the assistant warehouse manager were making. The pay of these two managers had fallen behind that of the supervisors for whom they were responsible. Lennon said that the men had a good case but pointed out that any increase of pay for them would have been illegal under Stage Two of the Incomes Policy which was then in force. He was told to combine the two jobs.

'In that way, you can sack one and promote the other.'

Markland later pointed out the lesson of this to Leyland by saying: 'If you stop to think things out there is always a solution.'

It had never occurred to him that the two men worked in widely separated parts of the factory and performed quite different functions. The idea that these jobs could be combined was, for these reasons, an absurdity. He remained oblivious to this and to the fact that the services of both men were retained, but in his own mind he firmly believed that he had made a decision. In fact, he took some satisfaction in the swashbuckling style of management which it typified.

He classified himself as a member of the officer class. He seemed to believe that as such he was entitled on impulse to perform extravagant pranks. Later on, he had the idea that the sales campaign, which was being launched by Palmer and Smith, could be made more eye catching and, therefore, more effective with the help of several suitably contoured young ladies. Palmer and Smith showed much enthusiasm for his idea. Without hesitation Markland commissioned a leading London fashion house to design appropriate uniforms for the sales-girls. He had the further idea that they could be provided with cars which were painted in colours which matched their uniforms. In a moment of abandonment, he drove one of the more curvacious of the new recruits around the Leeds factory mounted on a fork lift truck. This caused great amusement among the workers and served to enhance him in their eyes. The paradox of his officer class attitudes would have been shown had a worker performed such a prank. He would, almost certainly, have approved the instant dismissal of the man.

He believed that his military experience had provided him with the leadership skills which were the basis of successful man-management. He also held the view that he had at business school acquired a knowledge of modern management techniques which complemented these leadership capabilities. At this school he had been inundated with written matter. In order to cope with the large volume of paper work to which they were subjected, he and his fellow students attended classes on the art of quick reading. At frequent intervals he had been required to produce, at speed, reports on problems which were described in case studies taken from the 'live' world of business. The way in which these reports were presented was considered to be quite as important as their content. The reports themselves followed a typical format. This consisted of a summarized restatement of the problems described in the case studies followed by a list of recommended actions. His experience at business school taught him the art

38

of combining written work with graphs and statistical data. The lesson which he drew from this experience was that the capacity to generate and absorb vast quantities of paper work was an essential ingredient in successful modern management.

At business school, he had spent a great deal of time working on case studies in small groups of students. The idea that management was a group activity was also fostered by role playing exercises and by business games. Typically, groups of students would imagine that they were boards of directors dealing with real business problems. These groups were constituted so that they contained, wherever possible, at least one student with some formal training in accountancy. This subject had great symbolic importance to staff and students alike, because it was believed that businesses existed primarily to make money. Again, the science of management accounting was thought, by them, to be of paramount importance because it reduced, or claimed to reduce, all the activities which take place in a company to commensurate terms, that is, to money values. According to this ideology, management accounting provided the principal tool whereby those in charge of companies could assess and guide what went on in them. Management controls were thought to be practically coincident with accountancy procedures.

His lack of contacts at Tufted made it probable that he would try to communicate with others primarily through formal channels. The indoctrination of the business school, plus the reinforcing experience of his work in staff departments, converted this probability into a near certainty. Not surprisingly, he also attached overwhelming importance to the system of management accountancy, with its attendant budgets which he had helped to install at Tufted. The approval that the chairman had shown in connection with his work served as further confirmation of the validity of the system. In his mind, the masses of data which were now being produced by the accounts department of Tufted, represented a crucial breakthrough. He never felt that these data were misleading or fictitious. His devotion to this system and his absorption in paperwork led him to make one-sided assessments of the directors at Tufted. The inability of these directors to generate and handle impressive amounts of paperwork conditioned his assessment of them.

He also responded to his isolation by staging spectacular theatrical events. For instance, within two days of his appointment as managing director, he called a crisis meeting of resident directors in order to lecture them on the details of the previous month's management accounts. The fact that some of them had to be recalled from holiday added to the theatricality of the occasion. The proclivity to stage theatrical events was much more a product of his own personality than of his past training and experience.

Already, almost within days of his appointment, the pattern of future events had been set in Markland's response to the overwhelming fact of his isolation. His resort to petty restrictions, his commitment to formality and paperwork, his aggressive posturing, the peremptory tones of his communications, his over-extended commitments to Muldoon and Palmer, his obsession with the accounting system, and his passion for theatricality all served to intensify the isolation which was an integral part of his situation. This pattern of behaviour was to be replicated over and over again in the months ahead.

It must not be assumed that these responses imposed decisive handicaps on Markland in his attempt to make a success of his new appointment. There is no way in which the operational and social isolation which chief executives experience can be adequately overcome. In fact, the barriers to open relationships which are experienced in all organizations serve to maintain within them the credibility of those in positions of authority. In the absence of taboos on certain kinds of interaction those in authority would be seen to be like all other men. They would be seen to combine intelligence with stupidity. The pretensions of those in authority would be seen to be comic in the extreme. The privileges which they enjoy over their subordinates would seem to have little, if any, justification. Under these circumstances, organizations would, as we know them, cease to exist. All social systems—including business organizations—ultimately derive their cohesion from the beliefs of their participants.

Markland's dilemma was that he had to pierce the barriers to communication sufficiently to find out what actually went on at Tufted Carpets while at the same time he needed to maintain or even strengthen them so as to preserve his own authority.

5
Appointment of a consultant

Teacher and student

When Markland first went to business school he had some serious problems with his studies. His personal tutor, George Gray, recognized that these were not due to any lack of innate ability. He spent much time and effort helping him to overcome initial difficulties and it pleased him when Markland eventually overtook most of those who already had degrees.

Gray was sensitive to the problems of the non-graduate student. Before he went to university at the age of 25 he had been an assembler at an aircraft factory; he knew exactly how hard it could be for the mature student to get into the swing of things at college. After his experience in the factory it seemed to him as though the lifestyle of the dons was infinitely more agreeable, and he resolved to become one himself. After achieving this for several years he entertained the hope of becoming a professor, but further advance eluded him. He was slowly coming to terms with the fact of his own failure, but more than a trace of bitterness and resentment remained in his make-up. Even so, his thwarted ambition had not yet been entirely extinguished; it continued to smoulder deep inside him. The drive behind his ambition had been insecurity. The partial abatement of that ambition had hardly diminished his sense of insecurity.

The relationship between himself and Markland had been friendly, but the latter had not been one of his favourites. He was therefore rather surprised when Markland visited the College and hinted very strongly that he might shortly be in a position to offer him a consultancy. At that time Markland had been made responsible by his company for some in-house management training programmes and came to ask his former tutor's advice about the organization of these. Nothing came of the consultancy suggestion, but Gray did obtain the impression that his former student was most anxious to do him a good turn and had felt that way ever since leaving college.

A telephone call
It was late morning, Gray sat in his college office, conscious of little more than the unexpected and comforting warmth of the late autumn sunshine which streamed in through the half-open window. His reverie was disturbed by a telephone call. He was surprised to hear the voice of a young lady with a pleasant Yorkshire accent.

'I've got Mr David Markland, the managing director of Tufted Carpets, on the line for you.'

He was half consciously absorbing the social meaning of this introduction when he heard the instantly recognizable tones of his former student. After some personal exchanges Markland said:

'We're having a spot of bother with the unions here. If you're not too busy you might be able to help.'

'Delighted. What about expenses?'

'No trouble.'

On the following morning Gray put on his only suit, which had become much too tight around his waist. He did not own an attaché-case. For years he had made do with a zipped bag of the sort which are popular among undergraduates. Thus attired and equipped he set out on his journey. In spite of these efforts at sartorial elegance he hardly looked the part.

The interview
He was met by a company chauffeur at Leeds City Station. Shortly afterwards he found himself being ushered into the managing director's presence. The latter barely inclined his head in acknowledgement. Without as much as a glance at the new arrival he continued to address a secretary who stood attentively at the side of his desk.

'Which papers are for signature and which for decision?'

Instructions of this kind continued for several moments without pause, except for brief acknowledgements and supplications on the part of the secretary. Meanwhile, Gray felt absurd and awkward just standing there. Without invitation he sat down on a chair at the far side of the room. After the departure of the secretary Markland beamed confidently across his desk. He leant back in his swivel chair with an expansive gesture. Gray felt uncomfortable at the reversal of their former roles and was first to speak. He congratulated his former student on the speed and magnitude of his success.

'Quite some place you have here.'

Markland brushed this imperiously aside. He indicated that his job was no more than a temporary staging post on the way to higher things in Total Furnishings. He asserted that in a couple of years or so he would be moved back to head office with a greatly increased

42

responsibility. Gray felt that he had lost the first round by a large margin.

Some brief exchanges of personal news helped to relax the tension, Markland was the first to get down to business. He began by describing the walk-outs and work-to-rules which recently had become regular occurrences at Tufted. He continued by explaining how he had addressed mass meetings of workers in an attempt to remedy the situation. The rationale behind these exhortations was that they would serve to communicate directly to the workers and have the effect of raising their morale. Gray shuddered inwardly at the thought of him parading Blimpish attitudes before crowds of workers and said:

'You should keep your distance. You should only intervene as a last resort.'

Markland enquired about his college commitments and how much time he might be able to devote to Tufted. Gray estimated that he would probably be able to spend a day or two each week at Tufted. At this point Markland raised the question of fees.

'You know all about the scales used by consultancy firms. How much do you think I should pay you for each visit?'

In the past Gray had underpriced his services. He had by now learned that most people took one at one's own evaluation; he therefore named a substantial figure. Markland did not show any concern and at once agreed to this amount.

Gray felt slightly cheated and immediately went on to the attack by asking about expenses. These were then listed—hotel charges, incidental expenses, first class rail fares, and a car mileage allowance. These were to be claimed from the managing director's secretary on a visit-by-visit basis.

Markland then directed the conversation toward what might be involved.

'How are you going to set about your work?'

'I'll have to get to know the managers, the shop stewards, and the place generally. Until I've done that I won't be in a position to offer detailed advice, and even then I can't guarantee practical results.'

'Why don't you pretend to be a student gathering material for a research project or something? In that way people won't identify you with management and they will speak to you more freely.'

'That's not on. It's spying. There would be no end of trouble if I were found out. I must operate in the open under my true colours.'

Markland shrugged his shoulders.

'That's a pity, but I suppose you're right.'

After some further prompting Gray said:

'I need to know how much each category of labour is paid. I need to know how their pay packets are made up. I need to know how differentials have moved in this place over the past year or two. This is basic. I need to know much else besides.'

Markland began to look a little pale and he showed for the first time some impatience with his visitor. He indicated that there were procedures for dealing with industrial relations disputes and expressed the expectation that Gray would select those appropriate to Tufted. There had been, he said, some pressure from the unions to set up a joint shop stewards committee. He suggested that he would like him to devise a constitution and a set of rules for such a committee. He also showed much enthusiasm for shop stewards' courses and seemed to think it self-evident that these would do much to reduce industrial conflict at Tufted by improving communications. He asked Gray to advise on the selection of these.

Gray replied that although these things might be useful they did not, in themselves, constitute an answer to the industrial relations problem at Tufted. He expressed the opinion that it was necessary to address problems directly rather than worry about procedural niceties and other forms of window dressing. He concluded with the following ultimatum:

'There aren't any glib answers to the problems you've got here on the shop floor. Either I do the job in my own way or not at all. You can call the whole thing off if you want.'

The managing director's look of alarm had by now changed to one of disbelief.

'You're in the wrong ball park. You know the name of the game as well as I do.'

Gray returned a blank look of incomprehension so Markland continued:

'Profit, that's what it's all about. The chairman wants me to make a million this year. I won't get any credit for doing the sort of thing you've got in mind. The way you are intending to carry on I would be left running the perfectly organized factory which never made any money at all.'

He told his visitor that he had already taken a big step towards ensuring that Tufted made profits by adjusting 'margins', 'volume variances', and 'the product mix'. Gray did not understand this accounting jargon, but he had the premonition that the managing director had lost touch with empirical realities.

Markland reminded Gray of his own theories.

'You always used to say that factories more or less run themselves and that it is a mistake to believe that managers control what goes on in them on a day-to-day basis. Now you're telling me to do the opposite and try to make a real job of running this place. I won't get any political mileage out of that. I'll be moving on in two years, and I've got to show quick results. The way to do that is to change prices and manipulate the accounts in one way or another. If I show good financial results it won't matter what sort of mess I leave behind on the shop floor for my successor to clean up.'

Gray paused, and looked straight at him to force some kind of decision.

'I can't see how you are going to achieve anything unless you get the men working properly.'

Markland turned away and while looking out of the window said:

'OK have it your way. We'll try an experiment. Let's do what you've said is impossible. Let's try to manage this place.'

Gray's reply was cut short by a polite knock on the door.

'I'll have to see my secretary for a moment or two.'

Gray offered to leave but was told to remain. The secretary handed the managing director a thick sheaf of papers in a decorative folder. Markland made some hurried corrections to what were evidently complex networks of graphs. He signed a separate letter which the secretary handed to him and immediately signalled her to leave. Gray asked what the large folder contained.

'It's the month's report to the chairman.'

In response to more questions he admitted that he wrote comparable reports every month and spent at least half of his time on this task.

Gray was tempted to say:

'How do you expect to know what goes on here when you spend so much time and effort on these reports?'

Instead, he said half jokingly:

'I thought for one moment that that was your doctoral thesis.'

The journey home

Gray felt pleased with himself on the train home that evening. He was in no mood for introspection. Had he been, he might have wondered why he had been shown such favour. It was obvious that Markland respected his tutor's feel for problems of industrial relations, but it was also equally obvious that the explanation lay much deeper. Gray had helped Markland, but he had done the same for all those students who both wanted help and were prepared to help themselves. Why was it that this student attached such disproportionate importance to his tutor's past efforts? Perhaps it was related to his loneliness and the fact that so few helping hands had come his way. Less charitably, it may have been that he resented his former dependency on

45

one who was so evidently not a member of the officer class. The inclusion of his tutor within the orbit of his patronage could have been an attempt to reassert the proper order of precedence. Whether these conjectures were well founded or not, Gray would have certainly agreed on one point: Markland took a boyish delight in his newly acquired patronage and he, for one, shared that enjoyment.

He did reflect, however, that he had found it difficult to get outside work. His colleagues in the business school were always boasting about how busy they were and how much they earned. He contemplated the pleasure of outdoing them at their own game. He had felt increasingly stifled by the passivity of his college duties; it would be good to do something more active. Markland, he thought, had done him a very good turn indeed.

His dinner on the train that evening tasted especially good, and he celebrated with a whole bottle of wine.

6
Long distance commuting

The first working visit

Gray decided to travel the 190 miles to Leeds by car. He felt as though he had already done a day's work by the time he arrived at the factory. As he entered Markland's office he exclaimed:

'I feel shattered. I'd love some tea and a bite to eat.'

The managing director was very considerate and at once rang for his secretary.

'I'd like tea for two and a plate of sandwiches for Mr Gray.'

The ritual of eating together established equality between the two, and for the moment they both felt a bond of friendship.

Markland was the first to talk business, but did so apologetically and with much more reluctance than usual. He suggested that the consultant might like to start by interviewing the personnel manager. After spreading an organization chart on his desk he indicated that he would later introduce him to the factory manager and the head of management services. They finished their refreshments and he led the way across the executive car park to a ramshackle outbuilding which contained the offices of the personnel manager and his assistant. As he left he called out:

'I'll see you in the boardroom for lunch!'

Gray was immediately struck by the decor of the personnel office. This was hardly surprising because the walls as well as the floor were thickly carpeted. He expressed his astonishment and made some jocular remarks. This helped to break the ice a little and he was thankful that the personnel manager was a ready talker. More so because the journey had left him fatigued and in no mood for work. He was quite prepared to listen to whatever the personnel manager cared to say. For quite a while he did little more than nod and express agreement.

After a while the personnel manager began to expound his personal philosophy on life in general and on trades unions in particular. Unions, he argued, were or should be unnecessary; they were a product of mismanagement.

'If I set up and developed a company and unions came in I'd know

47

that I'd failed to treat the men and women there properly. The folk here are basically decent and hard working. Of course, there is the occasional bad one, but you get them everywhere. They join unions because they aren't treated fairly and like human beings. Half the trade union officials are as bad or worse than any of the managers. Do you know, there's one of the local union leaders who tells me to sack the ringleaders whenever we have trouble here. He's like a gramophone record; he says the same thing over and over again. He just isn't interested.'

Gray feigned disgust and astonishment and the personnel manager began to speak with even more feeling, and a certain note of bitterness entered his voice. He agreed that line managers knew more about what went on on the shop floor than he could possibly hope to know. However, he asserted that they often agreed things without working out their wider implications. He went on to express regret at the fact that they did not take him more fully into their confidence.

'Sometimes I'm asked to meetings and sometimes I'm not. I'd not mind all that much except they always want me to bail them out when it's too late. I report to the production director. I should report directly to the managing director. That would give me the authority and standing I need to do my job properly.'

Gray cut the personnel manager short when he was in full cry because lunch-time was fast approaching. In businesslike tones he instructed:

'I want a file of all current trade union agreements, the dates of the most recent pay settlements in respect of each category of worker, the numbers employed, the names of shop stewards and their respective unions. I also want, urgently, to know what movements in differentials have taken place over the past year or two and what each category of labour actually earns at present. I'd also appreciate some notes describing recent disputes and those still in progress.'

The personnel manager was visibly taken aback by these demands and by the sudden change in Gray's demeanour, but he quickly recovered his composure and assured his visitor that the required information would be speedily forthcoming.

Over lunch the managing director introduced the newcomer to Palmer, Muldoon, Birtwhistle, and Lennon. Gray at once took a liking to Lennon who remarked, after Markland had explained that he was an industrial relations consultant:

'We certainly could do with some expertise and inspiration in that area.'

The afternoon was, from Gray's point of view, even less informative than the morning. He found the factory manager very hostile and completely unhelpful. His interview with the head of management services was more protracted. He formed a very unfavourable assessment of him and the work of his department which further experience served only to confirm. He sensed that this man regarded his presence as an intrusion. Markland had omitted to tell him that the head of management services was formally responsible for industrial relations policy.

The mill at Cleckheaton

Gray decided to make a couple of visits to the mill at Cleckheaton in order to get some impression of the place. On the first occasion he was introduced to the mill manager by the managing director's chauffeur. The mill manager, though new to the job, seemed to be an integral part of the mill itself. He explained to the consultant that he had worked in the carpet trade all his life and had been at the mill even when it belonged to a different company. He showed Gray around, explaining with obvious knowledge the intricacies of the production processes. He showed particular enthusiasm for the latest tufting machines. Gray barely understood most of what he was told, but was, nevertheless, greatly impressed. The mill manager, he thought, was far more able than any other person he had so far met at Tufted. After completing their tour, they enjoyed a cordial lunch together in a local pub.

On their return, Gray was introduced to the head of the production control office. He liked this man also, but was intensely bored by his description of the work of the office. The office walls were covered with charts, and clerks regularly adjusted the information which was displayed on them. The whole room reminded Gray of a military headquarters. He saw that the clerks were automatically following routines and felt sure that the displayed information did not reflect with any degree of accuracy what was taking place in the mill beyond.

The roads were icy when he next set out for Cleckheaton so he made his way to the station instead of the motorway. This forced change of plans disappointed him slightly because it meant that he had to forego the highly lucrative mileage allowance. The extra that he made by travelling second class while claiming at the first class rate offered only slight compensation.

When he arrived at the mill he was greeted by a receptionist who offered him a cup of tea and some biscuits. Her office, the whole of a large reception area, and the production control office were lushly carpeted in a deep pile of dark green hue. When he had finished his tea she suggested that he might like to use the production director's office. Lennon was out for the day with the mill manager visiting an exhibition of carpet-making machinery.

The office itself had a slightly faded but still impressive grandeur. It was much larger than any of those at Leeds. The walls were magnificently panelled in oak and the room was furnished with leather armchairs, a splendid desk, and a grandfather clock. He noticed that Birtwhistle's vacant office next door was similarly furnished. It seemed to him that these rooms were evocative of a past age of immense solidity and boundless confidence; they were made to last and had about them exactly the redolence which film and television producers try to capture in sets depicting the offices of bullying Victorian mill owners.

For a brief moment he walked outside and looked at the dingy red brick edifice with slate roofs. The mill reminded him of paintings by Lowry, as did the figures who entered and left it. He decided to go on a tour by himself for want of anything better to do. Without a guide he found that he had more time to linger on what he saw.

The floors were paved and uneven. In part of the main section some upper floors had been removed to reveal a sagging roof. In this dark cavern stood twenty tall tufting machines. Beyond this main section was a long narrow outbuilding which housed two steaming and stinking backing plants. Here the illumination and ventilation were particularly poor. It was obvious that the narrowness and lack of height in this building made it difficult for workers to move and handle rolls of carpet and other material.

He discovered a factory canteen which he had not been shown on his earlier visit. It was a long narrow room, in much need of redecoration, on an upper floor. Here meals and drinks were dispensed impersonally via a battery of coin operated machines. The place, he thought, offered little comfort or escape from the gloom of the work areas.

Gray tried to relieve the tedium which he felt, by taking a few jars and some sandwiches in a nearby pub. On his return to Lennon's office he exchanged a few words with the affable man from the production control office. Alone in Lennon's office he attempted to write a memorandum to Markland on his progress so far. It was a hopeless task; there was absolutely nothing to say. In despair he tried to read a newspaper but found that his eyes refused to move down the columns. Eventually, he took out his pocket chess set and passed away an hour or two before leaving to catch the fast evening train.

On the long journey home he had ample opportunity to reflect on the intrinsic futility of his visit, and he resolved to make a much greater effort to do something to justify his fees. He knew that he would be unable to stand many days like this one. However, over dinner on the train he began to realize that he had learnt some quite important things. He was beginning to understand that Cleckheaton was, in comparison with Leeds, a political wilderness. He also wondered what there was for Lennon to do when he had so capable a lieutenant in the shape of the mill manager.

Making contact

Understandably, his next visit was to the Leeds factory, but he was disappointed to find that Markland was out. After taking morning tea and buttered toast in the boardroom with Smith, he wandered down to the backing plant in the hope that he might be able to extract some information from the factory manager whose office was close by that department. Once again, he was disappointed; it was empty. While he was standing there wondering what on earth there was for him to do he heard a cheerful voice greeting him through the door. A diminutive figure introduced himself as John Taylor, the backing plant manager. In a few minutes Gray was guided to another office by his new acquaintance.

The backing plant manager seemed to be impressed by his visitor's status and was encouraged by the fact that he was a ready listener. The manager mentioned Wilfred Brown's book, *Piecework Abandoned*, which had, he said, made a deep impression on him. He was delighted that his visitor seemed to be familiar with its contents. For a couple or more hours he explained how the ideas expressed in the book could be applied advantageously to the backing plant. He expressed the opinion that the measured day work scheme which was being prepared by the management services department was much too complicated to be acceptable to the men. Gray broke off this discussion to take lunch in the boardroom, but before leaving he promised to return later in the afternoon.

The afternoon session was even more fruitful than the morning one. His new contact introduced him first to the shop steward of the backing plant and dyehouse, and then to the convener of shop stewards. These men were very informative, and, in due course, they introduced him to other stewards. At last he felt he was beginning to make progress and, subsequently, he spent much more time on the shop floor.

Progress report

One day after they had taken lunch together in the boardroom Markland called Gray into his office.

'How are you getting on?'

Gray reported that he had begun to make some useful contacts on the shop floor but expressed concern at the failure of both management services and personnel to provide him with basic information on earnings and differentials. Markland shared this concern, and asked the consultant to send him a written statement describing the information needed so that disciplinary action could be taken. Gray indicated that he would be sending him a memorandum in the next few days on industrial relations at Tufted. Among other things it would, he asserted, describe both the information required and the manner in which it should be presented.

The managing director became visibly angry when his consultant mentioned the ban on overtime working which was being enforced in the backing plant. He almost shouted:

'Do you realize that we're seriously down on budget last month because of the ban? How can I hope to run this place when this sort of thing is going on? I've a good mind to issue them all with written reprimands, and, if that doesn't work, then, I think we should suspend them for a few days so that they can cool off. We might as well close the place down as run at a loss.'

Gray replied:

'You can't discipline them for not working overtime because it's voluntary. Action of that kind would make a difficult situation impossible.'

Markland, who was still angry, barked:

'What would you do then?'

'It's better to do nothing rather than act foolishly. The men are already feeling the pinch, and as Christmas is fast approaching I'm sure they are looking for an excuse to call the ban off temporarily. If I were you I'd see that a conciliatory gesture was made so as to encourage the resumption of normal working.'

Markland's anger had by now subsided somewhat and he asked:

'What would you have me do then?'

'I'd put Lennon in charge of the negotiations. If you're going to make a conciliatory gesture you might as well use someone who can act the part.'

This suggestion proved almost too much for Markland who shouted:

'In God's name, can't you see he's a fool. Why don't we give the job to George Cuthbertson (the factory manager). He's tough and clear headed.'

'We don't need toughness right now. In any case, the men and stewards hate him and they like Lennon. I'm quite sure that I can point Lennon in the right direction.'

After a long pause Markland said:

'Well, I suppose we must have it your way.'

The consultant continued by describing how the incentives which management services had introduced in various sections had closed the £2 differential gap previously enjoyed by backing plant operatives over less skilled workers. He mentioned that in the last two months incentives had been introduced into 'goods in', 'dispatch', and 'pre-dyed stores'. Incentives, he pointed out, could not be introduced into the backing plant because that department was already on bonus.

'I've not been able to check on the £2 figure which the shop stewards are quoting because I can't get any sense out of those blasted staff departments of yours. I'm quite sure that the men are in no mood to settle for less. We know that it's illegal to give these men a straight increase so we've got to find a way of fiddling the pay structure. If you're not prepared to do this, then you can say good-bye to co-operation in the backing plant.'

Markland, more by gesture than words, indicated his agreement so Gray continued:

'The measured day work scheme now being prepared by management services is much too complicated, and it doesn't promise any extra money. It stands no chance of acceptance by the men. The head of management services tells me the scheme will be ready by March! He has no sense of realism or urgency. If we don't come up with something shortly I'm sure that the men will discontinue the routine maintenance work they're doing and for which, they say, they're not paid. Besides this, they're talking about stopping the machines during meal breaks.'

He continued to argue the point that it was essential to do everything possible to reach an agreement with the men after the lifting of the overtime ban.

'Otherwise, in the new year, it will be combined with a work-to-rule.'

By now he had managed to redirect the managing director's fury away from the men and towards the head of management services. As he was preparing to leave Markland said:

'I'll give that fellow a great big kick up the backside.'

7
Cold offices

Johnson's first day

Johnson arrived at Tufted just before nine o'clock on the appointed day early in November. His progress at the main gate at the Leeds factory was halted by a lowered barrier of the kind used on continental style railway crossings. Two of these spanned the entrance which was at least eighty feet wide. Between these was a gatehouse which invariably contained at least two security guards. He was obliged to leave his car and report to one of these. After a guard had confirmed by telephone that Howard Johnson was due to start work that morning, the barrier was raised. These elaborate precautions were routine, and made necessary by the existence of a ready market for carpet which 'fell off lorries'.

He parked his car in front of the office block and five minutes later was shown into Markland's office. After the exchange of formal greetings, he was given a single sheet of paper headed 'Business Planning and Operations Executive—Job Specification'. Under this was Johnson's name. The first paragraph formally stated that the post was responsible to the managing director and that its general purpose was to 'improve the operating efficiency of the company'. At the foot of the page were the enigmatic words—'to improve communications in the production department'.

Markland took Johnson on a brisk tour of the factory and introduced him perfunctorily to several of the more senior managers. On the completion of this tour he took him to a small office which was adjacent to his own. He gave Johnson a voluminous folder which contained a package entitled 'Management Accounts—October 1973', and said:

'I'll pick you up for lunch at 12.30 p.m. This afternoon we are having our regular management meeting, and I'd like you to be there.'

The room between the managing director's office and the boardroom was intended for a personal secretary. Markland had moved her to another office on the other side of the corridor so as to accommodate Johnson. The latter noted that it was carpeted in the same luxurious style as the two adjoining rooms. A small window looked out on a snow-capped hill, and in the foreground was an exceedingly ramshackle group of farm buildings. Immediately behind these was an elevated section of motorway which served to spoil the rural scene. The office itself was furnished with a desk, a chair, a filing cabinet, and a telephone. Johnson's circulation had been stimulated by the briskness of his walk, but within a few minutes he became aware of a numbing coldness. At the time government regulations forbade the use of electricity for space heating in offices. The small paraffin heater which had been placed in a corner of the office smelt a great deal but gave out precious little warmth. He contrasted this abject contraption with the large and efficient butane gas fire which heated Markland's office. He examined the desk drawers and the filing cabinet only to find that they were empty. After a few minutes he left his office briefly, to equip himself with the tools of his profession—paper and pencils, and then, in spite of the cold, he made an attempt to consider the contents of the folder.

The hands on his watch made slow and laborious progress towards lunchtime. An executive's first days are always difficult and when he is not even a member of a department they can be oppressively lonely. His only contact at this stage was the managing director himself and he felt unable to relieve his tedium by 'dropping in' on his boss for a chat.

After what seemed an eternity, the hands on his watch reached 12.30 p.m.—but relief in the shape of Markland did not come. By now the office had become like a prison cell and its walls seemed to be closing in on him. He tried to think about Lennon and Palmer— the two directors he had met on his second interview, but it was useless. The hardness of his chair and its lack of arms added to his discomfort. By the time the hands on his watch had reached one o'clock he felt as though he was suffering from exposure. A minute or two afterwards the door burst open and Markland swept into the office. He smiled broadly and queried:

'How are you getting on?'

Without waiting for an answer he continued:

'What do you think of our management accounts?'

'Fine.'

Johnson tried to put on an air of understanding and enthusiasm as he made this remark. However, the numbing cold had worn away his concentration and he unthinkingly added:

'They're a shade voluminous, and I'm not familiar with all the product names, but they do seem very detailed.'

'Good. Good. Let's lunch. I think that it would be better to go in your car.'

This instruction struck Johnson as slightly odd. They lunched in a pleasant restaurant in the countryside, some five miles from the factory. On the way back Johnson was directed to make a small detour so that Markland might view the cottage which he proposed to buy as a *pied à terre* near Leeds. In the car he had told Johnson that he intended to keep his flats in London and Edinburgh as well as his croft in the Highlands. The cottage itself was in an extraordinary state of disrepair. Why on earth, Johnson asked himself, is this man of evident means and property proposing to buy such a dilapidated structure? In his mind the interlude was fast acquiring a surrealistic quality.

They arrived back at the factory fifteen minutes late. In the boardroom everyone was huddled around the large butane stove which was normally in the managing director's office. Instructions had been left for this to be moved and put close to the large chair in the boardroom. As soon as they entered a pathway was cleared—it seemed by magic—to make way for Markland. After much shifting of chairs they all took their respective places. Markland, of course, sat in the large chair behind the desk at the head of the table. Johnson was obliged to sit at the opposite end of the room; he was as far from the sole source of heat as was physically possible, within the confines of the boardroom.

Markland ostentatiously took a folder from his briefcase, spread it before him on the desk, leaned forward with his elbows on the desk and with his head held erect said:

'You all received the note about Howard Johnson who has just joined us. I'm sure you would like to join me in welcoming him.'

The directors made some vague mumbling sounds and gave their impression of a welcoming smile.

'Let's get down to business then,' Markland said briskly, 'and find out why we made such a mess of October.'

The meeting dragged on throughout the afternoon. Markland and Smith sat next to each other and were comforted by the warmth of the stove while the rest of the board shivered. The proceedings themselves brought little enlightenment to Johnson. They were dominated by Markland who used the folder of accounts as an agenda. Johnson was puzzled by a strong call from him and Muldoon for the sales department to concentrate their selling effort on the most expensive ranges. The management accounts suggested that these had the highest margins both in terms of percentage and in terms of pence per square yard. Johnson noticed that these ranges represented only a trivial proportion of the company's output. Some disquiet was expressed by Lennon who doubted the capacity of the factories to make these lines in significant quantities. In spite of this muted protest a firm decision was reached to switch the sales effort away from the cheap carpets which the factories made in large quantities. Smith and Palmer endorsed the decision to change the salesman's incentive scheme so that it would now be personally unprofitable for them to sell the best selling lines. Johnson came away from the meeting with an uneasy feeling. Despite his short acquaintanceship with the company he felt that the decision taken could not possibly be right. The seeds were sown in his mind which led to a long and bitter campaign to challenge the dominance of the management accounts on Markland's thinking.

Johnson tries to find his bearings

Johnson was conscious that he might be perceived by the resident directors as a threat to their positions. In particular, he was aware that Lennon would regard him in this light. After all, he had been appointed specifically to improve communications in the 'production department'.

Lennon knew that Markland despised him. He saw that Johnson's arrival had weakened his position. He conjectured that Johnson had been deliberately recruited as a potential replacement for himself. It was part of his innate political skill that he managed to greet Johnson with a convincing display of warmth when the latter first visited his office. A less skilful politician would have accelerated, or made more probable, his own departure by reacting aggressively toward the newcomer.

Johnson too felt the delicacy of the position. The fact that his own office was immediately adjacent to that of the managing director indicated that he was in a privileged position. He sensed that his relationship with Lennon could be crucial to his being accepted by his new colleagues. It was in this spirit that he approached Lennon, and the warmth of the greeting encouraged him.

After preliminaries, he introduced the subject of the product range and the decision taken regarding it at the management meeting. Lennon was noncommittal, and he pursued the matter by saying:

'I don't know much about carpets, but the policy sounded to me as if it would be likely to cause enormous problems in your area.'

Lennon nodded his assent, and went on to remark that the marketing side always seemed to have the last word, and that he did not think that he could do anything about it.

'Besides,' he said, 'Muldoon's figures say that those carpets are more profitable.'

Johnson left the matter there as he could sense Lennon's reluctance to declare himself further.

During the next few days, he busied himself trying to learn something about the production processes used at Tufted. Lennon assisted him by readily introducing him to the plant managers and others involved in production. In spite of this, however, Lennon remained neutral and uncommitted in his relationship with Johnson.

At the end of his first week Johnson had little to show. His only tangible output was a series of flow-charts showing the operations performed in making carpets supplemented by some descriptive notes. He had met, formally, most of the senior managers in the production area, and he was beginning to form opinions about board members. Lennon and Gammage seemed friendly but uncommitted; Tenniswood was entirely neutral; Palmer, Birtwhistle, and Smith continued to be formal even though he saw them at least three times a day in the boardroom—over morning coffee, lunch, and afternoon tea. He had already formed a strong dislike for Muldoon whose pomposity he found unbearable.

Johnson and Leyland meet
Johnson was concerned about the proximity of his office to that of the managing director. He noticed that another office just down the corridor was unoccupied, and he asked Markland if he could take possession of this. His new office was less comfortable than the one he had vacated; it was constructed out of thin partitions which separated it from the production and stock control office. It afforded little, if any, privacy, and its lack of an outside window rendered it positively gloomy in the office lighting restrictions which were then in force. Its sole advantage was that it gave a semblance of independence from his patron.

Markland clearly did not understand Johnson's motive because on the following Monday, when Jack Leyland arrived he gave him the very office that Johnson had so hastily vacated. Leyland's introduction to the company was even briefer than that given to Johnson seven days earlier. The managing director greeted the new arrival formally and handed him a job specification. It was exactly the same as that given to Johnson except that his 'specific responsibilities' were to improve communications in the 'production control department' instead of 'production department'. After a minute or two the interview was abruptly terminated by Markland who called in Johnson and said:

'Show him the ropes.'

Before this meeting both men had considered that they were rivals,

58

and at first they approached each other with caution. Within a week, however, they had formed a friendship. They liked one another and their predicament was in many ways similar: they were both newcomers and they were equally dependent on Markland. In his first week, Johnson had no one to talk to in a relaxed fashion. Leyland's arrival filled the gap.

Johnson had been invited to make full use of the boardroom, but he had been given no indication whether the same privilege was to be extended to Leyland. He foresaw a certain embarrassment for Leyland if he introduced him into the boardroom contrary to Markland's intentions. As the coffee break approached he felt more and more unsure about what to do. In the end, he decided to fabricate an excuse for both of them to visit the managing director in his office. The problem was solved when Markland led them both into the boardroom.

The two spent most of the rest of the week together, and they formed the habit of discussing anything which either wished to raise with Markland. In this way the foundations of an alliance were laid.

Getting accepted
Lennon was easy going and Johnson could find excuses to visit him at Cleckheaton without giving the appearance of always looking over his shoulder. These little outings provided him with an escape from the tedium and inactivity of his office. Tenniswood's occupation was much more sedentary than Lennon's. Most of his transactions with suppliers were conducted on the telephone. When Leyland visited him he found that conversation had to be fitted in between calls. Tenniswood made no attempt to lessen the intrusion of telephone calls during his visits. Indeed, he seemed to prolong his calls deliberately. He got the impression that Tenniswood deeply resented his presence and he therefore made attempts to find out about stocks and production control from some of the more subordinate staff.

Leyland tried to make use of computer printouts as a source of information. The machine had originally been acquired to calculate and print invoices and maintain the company's sales ledgers. The computer was in Muldoon's department and he was ambitious to extend the scope of its operation. Over the past year it had been decided to use it to maintain records of finished stock and work-in-progress. Eventually, Muldoon hoped that his department would be made responsible for the compilation of material to be used for production planning. Leyland was presented with an enormous quantity of computer printout by the data processing manager. He was assured by him that it gave a complete and detailed picture of the current position. A cursory examination seemed to indicate that it contained all the information necessary for production control. At first, Leyland was surprised that he had seen no evidence of it in Tenniswood's section. His surprise was short lived; he quickly learnt that the information on the printouts bore little relation to physical realities in the warehouse and elsewhere. He asked Muldoon why this was so. He was told that the system was good but that production staff were incapable of following the simplest instructions and procedures. The system relied on a number of pre-punched cards being attached to each roll of carpet as it was tufted. These cards were to be returned at subsequent stages in production so that the computer could record the progress of each item. Leyland had a great deal of experience with computers. This combined with his observations on the factory floor convinced him that the procedure could not work unless the data collection system was completely redesigned. Wisely, he kept his own council and only voiced his opinion privately to Johnson. After some discussion they decided to mention some of their reservations about the system to Markland who immediately authorized Leyland to spend more time on these problems and look at other computer systems that might be used.

At this time Markland was deeply committed both to the extension of the computer's scope at Tufted and to the further elaboration of the management accounting system. The accounts themselves were produced manually, but there were plans in hand to change this. A team from head office had been studying the preparation of accounting data at Tufted and at other subsidiaries. The result had been the placing of orders for larger and more powerful computers, one of which was to be installed at Tufted. Muldoon had already been recruiting systems analysts and programmers for the new machine. Muldoon and Markland were both committed to the new computer, although the latter did not give the slightest indication of this to Johnson and Leyland. However, neither at that time, nor subsequently, did he impose any restrictions on his two advisers nor prevent them from looking at any part of the operation even when the results of their investigations could be potentially embarrassing to him.

Johnson found Lennon increasingly co-operative and gradually they began to form a kind of friendship. Several times during his second week they enjoyed a pint together after work in the pub outside the Leeds factory. By the end of the week he felt able to talk to Lennon about his reservations concerning the accounting system and his growing dislike for Muldoon. Lennon in return described problems in his own area. Neither of them thought it politic to discuss Markland.

Johnson knew of the latter's antipathy toward Lennon and he quickly came to the conclusion that this was entirely misplaced.

By the time another week or so had passed both Johnson and Leyland began to feel more at home. When Markland was in a good humour his sharp and ready wit gave rise to bursts of genuine laughter in the boardroom. On other occasions the results were less pleasing. For instance, once Lennon dared to disagree with Markland and he suffered the following rebuff:

'Ten years spent heading muddy footballs must have blunted your powers of reasoning, Stuart.'

Lennon was deeply affronted, and he responded by falling into an uncharacteristic silence in the managing director's presence. On other occasions, the brutality of Markland's rejoinders wounded other members of the board to the quick, but their ingrained submissiveness in the face of authority was such that they suffered these insults without protest. Sometimes, they even contrived to show some outward amusement at their own discomfort. Johnson and Leyland were treated with much more leniency. They, alone, in the boardroom were allowed to contradict Markland and could even argue with him at length without incurring his displeasure. Of course, they drew a distinction between what could be said to him in public and what might be said to him in private. Paradoxically, their open dissent was itself a form of ingratiation. However, it was clear to all in the boardroom that Markland had placed these two in a special category: they were his team; he had selected them, and he accepted them as intellectual equals.

When Markland was not in the boardroom the atmosphere was noticeably more relaxed. Johnson and Leyland began to feel that they were coming to be accepted even though the resident directors continued to treat them with caution because of their closeness to the managing director. Lennon had made certain minor disclosures to Johnson, but none of the other directors made the slightest effort to take the newcomers into their confidence; they were not admitted to the secret grapevines which had developed over the years in the boardroom.

Smith had a fund of salesman's anecdotes which everyone else had heard at least a dozen times before, however, he repeated them again for their benefit. Muldoon would solicit their opinion on some imagined weakness in the organization which had been brought to light by the management accounting system. Birtwhistle would describe to them the real or alleged properties of various sorts of carpet. Even Palmer would occasionally include them in his conversation, but he showed by looks rather than words that he viewed them with suspicion and hostility. The two were very inexperienced in the intricacies of board-room life, and as a result they were inclined to accept too readily the genuineness of any friendliness that was shown towards them. The support of Markland was reassuring but not enough; they both felt a need to be generally accepted.

8

Formation of an alliance

Lunchtime altercation

Markland was absent when Johnson and Leyland first encountered Gray, and in his absence, Palmer had chosen to symbolize his superiority by sitting at the head of the table. On his left sat Johnson while on the other side, nearest the door, sat Leyland and Muldoon. They were halfway through their lunch when Gray entered and sat down on the nearest convenient chair which happened to be next to Muldoon. The latter saw the enquiring looks on Johnson's and Leyland's faces and said:

'May I introduce George Gray. He's here to advise on industrial relations.'

As an afterthought he said:

'He teaches at David's old business school.'

Leyland could see little of the newcomer because Muldoon's considerable bulk obscured his view, but Johnson sat almost directly opposite him and was at once struck by his eccentric appearance. He had long greying hair which conveyed a wild impression and he wore a jacket and trousers of different checks. Never before had he seen a consultant who remotely resembled the visitor. He took an immediate dislike to his air of intellectualism and superiority which, he thought was typical of business academics. Others might have regarded the visitor as a rather comic, if not pathetic, character, but Johnson felt differently; he felt slightly threatened by him.

Johnson's opening remarks were faintly hostile and throughout the rest of the meal the conversation was competitive. It centred on the minor privileges which the staff enjoyed over the hourly paid. The consultant contrasted the comfort of the boardroom with the lack of amenities in the factory canteen. He mentioned other things such as the longer holidays and the superior toilet facilities which the staff enjoyed over the workforce. These marks of privilege he asserted, were essential to preserve authority. Johnson accepted all the perks of his position: for instance, he never thought twice about filling his petrol tank from the company pump on Friday afternoon so that he would not need to buy petrol for his weekend family outings, but his

63

conventional upbringing and his abstract commitment to social equality combined to give him a slight feeling of guilt about this sort of thing. Gray talked at length about the necessity and desirability of these privileges and Johnson disputed this viewpoint by quoting his experience in American industry where the petty status differences which were such a feature of British firms were less in evidence. He argued that this practice was desirable and should be adopted here. In support of this contention he quoted some passages from Robert Townsend's book, *Up the Organization*, which had influenced him considerably. Gray dismissed this as a source of authority, although he had not read the book in question. He said:

'I can't stand all that Christian name hypocrisy which the Americans go in for. That sort of thing only goes skin deep.'

After lunch in the relative privacy of his office, Johnson said to Leyland:

'What a twit!'

Leyland agreed. Gray's opinion of Johnson was scarcely more charitable. He thought him to be vain, opinionated, and pompous. He especially disliked his smooth, yet slightly flashy, appearance. He had come across his sort before and had coined the expression 'conspicuous executives' to describe them. They were a species which seemed to be especially attracted by the business school in which he worked. There were vast numbers of them in the South East of England, but here, in the North, they were thinner on the ground.

Reconciliation

Late in the afternoon, Markland's secretary telephoned Johnson with the news that Gray had been booked into the same hotel as himself. She added that as Gray was without transport, Markland had suggested that he might like to give him a lift. The prospect of an evening with Gray filled Johnson with dismay and he privately resolved to make some excuse to avoid him after their arrival at the hotel.

When they set out it was raining heavily, and this meant that Johnson had to concentrate on the task of driving. After a while they emerged from dimly illuminated roads onto a broad well-lit thoroughfare. At the same time the rain eased and both men felt the social pressures which force a conversation to start. Until then hardly a word had been exchanged.

Surprisingly, there was little tension between the two and their conversation, although formal, was uncompetitive. Neither felt inclined to restart their lunch hour debate. In the boardroom they had an audience, and the fire and fury of their debate had been something akin to the showmanship of gladiators. Strangely, now that they were alone neither felt the slightest need to impress the other.

Johnson explained something about his career before he came to Tufted. His companion responded by describing his own work at the university in somewhat deprecatory terms. He added that he had been Markland's personal tutor. Johnson at once became alert to the political implications of this casual remark, and for a minute or so both men reverted to silence. Suddenly, for want of something better to say, Gray said:

'Muldoon gave me a copy of last month's management accounts today.'

Johnson was tempted to give his opinions about these, but he held back and asked:

'What do you think of them?'

Gray beat about the bush for a minute or so, but eventually said:

'I don't know the first thing about accountancy, but they do seem to me to be a bit on the bulky side.'

After further prompting, he added:

'I can't quite see the point of calculating thousands of notional quantities to the third decimal point of a penny. I must confess that I'm mystified by the terminology of the accounts.'

Johnson now felt sure of his man and said:

'You're not mystified at all. You know it's all bloody nonsense.'

His companion burst into loud laughter and exclaimed:

'You're right. I don't think I've ever seen crap piled so high in my life before.'

Johnson had to concentrate on his driving once more as they crossed a busy intersection, and for the moment they reverted to silence. Gray was first to speak. He asked:

'How do you spend your time?'

'Drawing flowcharts and talking to people.'

'What sort of flowcharts?'

'You know, little boxes for each process and arrows showing the sequence of these processes.'

'Why do you do that?'

Johnson paused for a second, pondering that question.

'I don't know really. It's something I always did as a consultant—it seemed to be expected of me—I carry on doing it, I suppose, because I can't think how else to fill my time.'

On the face of it these were astounding disclosures for him to have made. He had only been in the company for just over a couple of weeks and regarded himself as very highly paid. Why did he take such risks? He hardly knew a thing about Gray other than that he was a friend of his boss. Such confessions of incompetence might be made between close friends who have no working relationships, but even then, they are only usually made after inhibitions have been reduced through the consumption of alcohol. However, it was very surprising that he should have made these remarks after the slightest of acquaintanceships to a friend of Markland's while stone cold sober. Admittedly, Gray had earlier described his own work in rather unfavourable terms and this had encouraged further disclosures, but Johnson had in the past committed many such indiscretions. So far he felt that Lady Fortune had smiled on him. He did not consider himself to be one of the stars of industry, but he had reached the boardroom at Tufted at a time when many of his contemporaries were beavering away at much more mundane levels. They, he thought, had not progressed all that far even though they always closed their lips to the truth. He did not see why, at this stage of his career, he should copy them by donning the all-enveloping mantle of hypocrisy which was worn by the archetypal up-and-coming executive. In this respect he resembled both Gray and Markland. All three shared a naive self-confidence which was to play a large part in the events which followed.

Fortune smiled again on this occasion. If Gray had been a different sort of person he would have stored these disclosures in his memory for use against Johnson on a later occasion. He did not; he was affected by their frankness and he, in turn, felt he could drop his guard completely.

Gray changed the direction of the conversation by launching an attack on Palmer. He denounced, somewhat to Johnson's surprise, this director in the most uncompromising and uncomplimentary terms. Although Johnson did not particularly like Palmer he thought that his companion was overdoing it so he said:

'Palmer seems to know his job.'

Gray said harshly:

'What is his job?'

Johnson was reduced to silence. His companion's next remark struck him as very odd, but he was impressed by its forthrightness.

'I think he could be a threat to Markland. I've got a feeling about him.'

Much to Johnson's delight his companion continued by redirecting his attack towards Muldoon. In this case, however, Gray's severe strictures were tempered with a certain humour.

By the time they reached the hotel there was no doubt that they had become firm friends; they went straight to the bar for a quick drink, and then took the shortest of breaks to check into their respective rooms. After dinner they went to the bar and there swapped anecdotes and indiscretions.

Gray commented on the difficulties he was having in gaining even the most rudimentary information about pay differentials, and he expressed his contempt for the staff specialists he had met in management services and personnel. Somewhat more tentatively he introduced the idea that Tufted was overstaffed.

'You know, every time I go into the works I find coffee mornings or afternoon tea parties being held in the factory manager's office. He seems to have seven or eight managers there discussing the most trivial subjects. I've even seen that number of managers arguing with a couple of shop stewards. It seems to me that the place is terribly overstaffed. There are so many managers and staff men that they cannot possibly have enough work to do; they just get in each other's way. That's why there's so much quarrelling going on in the place. I don't quite know what can be done about it. It's not really my pigeon.'

It was all so obvious that Johnson was astonished that he had not immediately come to the same conclusion himself. He had noticed that there was a surprising number of people scattered around the management hierarchy with few apparent functions, but somehow or other he had failed to draw the obvious conclusion. He produced a whole series of observations which served to confirm overstaffing but mocked his companion for his hesitancy.

'You know bloody well what's got to be done; they've got to go.'

'Of course, you're right. I'll have a word with David.'

By the end of the evening, they both felt that they had known each other for a long time, and their earlier clashes in the boardroom were completely forgotten.

The following day, Johnson recounted the evening to Leyland and after Gray had joined them for lunch, off the premises, an alliance was formed which lasted for the remainder of their time at Tufted.

9
Investigation and diagnosis

Industrial relations—the problem of information
On his first working visit, Gray had asked the personnel manager to provide him with information about earnings and recent changes in differentials at Tufted. A week or so afterwards he had received a copy of a list of earnings in a particular week for a random sample of workers. This had been prepared some months earlier as a matter of routine. It did not provide the information which was sought, because it failed to separate the amounts attributable to overtime. Nor did there seem any reason to believe that the amounts quoted were, in any sense, representative. Again, several categories were not included at all in the list.

Gray quickly gave up the attempt to extract useful information from the personnel manager. Instead, he directed his efforts at the head of management services. This manager did not even provide token information, and he protested that his department was already fully stretched preparing a measured day work scheme for implementation in the backing plant at Leeds. Gray complained to Markland about this lack of co-operation. Subsequently, on 6 December he sent him a memorandum on industrial relations at Tufted. Among other things it made the following points:

▶ At Tufted there is a lack of accessible and easily understandable information in respect of labour relations. This, in part, arises from the lack of any clear definition of responsibilities in this area. I would suggest that the following initial steps be taken:
1. The dates of the last wage settlements in respect of each category of employee should be listed. This is necessary because an increase can be granted under Stage Three only if 12 months have elapsed since the previous award. On the assumption that Stage Three will continue to operate, it will be necessary to consider in advance the implications of claims for each work category.
2. At intervals—say every three months—a wage comparison should be made covering all sections of wage earners and lower staff

categories. This comparison would give the gross average wage earned by each group over a standard working week. This comparison should be presented in chart form so that relative pay positions can be taken in at a glance. The gross amounts, in turn, should be divided into their component elements. This information too should be presented in a form designed for easy assimilation. Material of this kind would enable one to see how differentials were moving and the changing importance of the various pay elements in each work section. This information would be invaluable both for negotiating purposes and for planning.'

In spite of continued pressure from both Markland and Gray, the head of management services failed to provide this information. Eventually Markland sent a stiff memorandum to the head of management services with copies to Lennon, Cuthbertson (the factory manager), the personnel manager, Johnson, and Gray. It was entitled 'Wages/Bonus/Measured Day Work Schemes', and was dated 24 January 1974. It read:

► I do not want ANY further work done on any Payment Scheme of any sort whatsoever, for anybody in Tufted—to be touched, looked at, thought about, considered or anything else until I have seen a chart of the movement of wage and payment differentials over the past twenty-four months, and other information requested in the memo from George Gray on 6 December and endorsed in my memo of 12 December.

In spite of this plain language the management services department continued to fail to furnish the required information. Gray began to physically occupy this department on his visits in order to ensure compliance. At first he had assumed that the lack of co-operation was solely due to resentment of his intrusion into the area of industrial relations, an area previously in the domain of management services. At the time Gray had been unaware of this. He also did not then know that someone in the boardroom had told staff in this department of certain disparaging remarks that Gray had made about their boss. He never discovered who this person was, but was nevertheless hurt by this betrayal. He had every right to feel aggrieved as this represented a very serious breach of the conventions governing the boardroom. The head of management services had ample reason to feel hostile towards Gray.

Gray also discovered further reasons why the information had not been forthcoming. The staff of the department were very hard working and their time was fully absorbed in routine paperwork and in preparing elaborate pay schemes on predetermined lines. They responded to the stress, which Gray's arrival had helped to create, by working still harder at what they were already doing. This work provided not only the rationale justifying the existence of the department itself, it was also a source of professional and self esteem to its members. The consultant, backed by the authority of the managing director, instructed them to desist from such activity.

Absorption in routines did not represent an escape from work; it represented rather an attempt to avoid thought, through work. Thought might lead a person to question the value of what he and his colleagues were doing, and it could be extremely painful to those who were unaccustomed to it. One of the reasons why it is so difficult to engineer rational change in an organization lies in the entrenched resistance to thought.

Gray found that the department was incapable of producing the bar charts which he required. A certain amount of common sense and detachment were needed in their preparation. For instance, it was overlooked in the comparison that the length of the standard working week varied. Some categories worked 37½ hours, while others worked 40 hours. One group actually worked 42 hours. Again, overtime earnings were included in spite of repeated injunctions that this should not be done.

A few weeks later, after redundancy had eliminated all but two of the most junior members of this department, Gray found that the requisite bar charts were produced in less than a week under his guidance. Until then management had attempted to negotiate with the shop stewards in the absence of reliable data on earnings.

Industrial relations—the backing plant

For some time after Gray's arrival the backing plant at the Leeds factory provided the focal point of industrial conflict at Tufted. After making contact with the supervisors and shop stewards in this section he gradually built up an understanding of the causes underlying the recurrent disputes. In the months before his arrival the management services department had introduced several bonus incentive schemes in various sections of the factory on a piecemeal basis. The backing plant operatives had, before these schemes were introduced, enjoyed about a £2 differential over workers in other sections. Strictly speaking, the incentive schemes were a breach of the statutory incomes policy, but it never occurred to anyone that this was so. Similarly, a lieu bonus had been introduced for staff who belonged to the Supervisors' Union. A technical case could be fabricated to support the contention that the former incentive schemes were consistent with Incomes Policy, but the lieu bonus scheme was a clear breach. However, there was not the slightest awareness of this among senior managers and directors.

The head of management services argued that it was illegal to pay the men in the backing plant any more, and it was not possible to introduce incentives into this section because it was already on bonus. Management services attempted to assuage the discontent in the backing plant by promising to introduce a measured day work scheme. This scheme was complicated and did not guarantee any increase in pay. The provisional proposals presented by management services served only to inflame feelings in the backing plant.

Gray found out in his discussions with shop stewards in the backing plant that there was a widespread desire to simplify and consolidate the wage system. On 18 December, he wrote a letter to the managing director which described some of the problems in the backing plant.

▶ As you know, the men in the backing plant banned overtime on weekends and this was followed by further action which involved both a ban on meal break working and a work-to-rule. This last action consisted in working to the standard speeds laid down by the technical staff in conjunction with line management. In response to a request from management this action has been withdrawn in anticipation of the short-time working in the new year. . . .

The men in the backing plant feel that their true worth is not recognized by the company. It is true that the reject rate has fallen over the past two and a half years or so, while at the same time output has increased and down-time has fallen. The men in the backing plant also seem to undertake work outside their normal duties without extra payment. I understand that they have helped with dispatch, splitting, cutting, and various other tasks. I am also informed that they undertake a good deal of the more routine maintenance work on their plant themselves. There have also been occasions on which these man have kept the plant going manually when certain mechanical failures occurred. This multi-skilled flexibility has been encouraged by the backing plant manager.

The feeling in the backing plant is that these things are not sufficiently recognized by management and that direct action became necessary because of poor channels of communications made worse by certain personality problems.

The men on the backing plant feel especially that they should not have the lowest, or one of the lowest, base rates in the plant. Mr Gill (the head of management services) is, as you know, intending to introduce a measured day work scheme in the backing plant. The intention at the moment seems to be that the meal break allowance plus a proportion of the production bonus would initially be consolidated into the base rate. Mr Gill seems to think that the men cannot be trusted sufficiently to maintain their standards of effort if the production bonus were to be withdrawn entirely, and this view is, I think, widely shared among senior management. However, for my own part, I believe that it is possible to go rather further than is suggested. In addition, I think the so-called attendance bonus might be recognized for what it is and consolidated into the base rate.'

The letter went on to advise the retention of the quality bonus largely because this was believed to be important by the backing plant manager. Gray had come to believe that some concessions to the view of supervisors were necessary in order to ensure their support in the battle against management services.

The day this letter was posted, the backing plant reimposed sanctions because of the failure of management to act on their grievances. Gray received an urgent telephone call from Lennon about what line should be taken in order to get a resumption of normal working. He recommended that the claims relating to one man down working, pump money, and tank money should be conceded without argument and said:

'These amounts are just peanuts. I wouldn't clean the tanks for £2 extra. You know it's a bloody awful job. It's been £2 for years, and they are only asking for £3.50. Why don't you make it £4?'

Lennon agreed.

'That sounds sensible to me.'

Gray went on:

'You must promise at least some measure of consolidation. You have simply got to agree to the consolidation of the meal break allowance and the attendance bonus. If I were you I would promise to consolidate at least a proportion of the production bonus. They will ask for a fall-back rate of £3.50. There is no point in resisting this because that is the amount of the fall-back in the other departments on incentives.'

He continued by mentioning that the shop stewards were talking about some merit payments as a way of closing the £2 differential gap. Lennon was less enthusiastic about this, and Gray agreed to write him a note on this proposal.

Lennon lost no time in implementing these suggestions, and he was able to get the backing plant working again with some degree of normality.

In the new year the backing plant manager suggested to Gray a way of fiddling the quality bonus so that the men would obtain the extra £2 which was at the root of their discontent. On 9 January, Gray wrote in the following terms to Markland:

▶ In my opinion, a wage increase is justified in the backing plant. As you know the company is already in breach of Stage Three because of the bonus award to the supervisors. It is my view that it is quite impossible to run the factory and observe the smallest details of Stage Three provisions. The company should, therefore, simply avoid open and flagrant breaches. In my opinion the easiest way to give the backing plant an increase would be to change the basis of calculation in respect of the quality bonus. Mr Taylor (the backing plant manager) has worked out a way of doing this which is likely to yield a wage increase over a standard working week of about £2. The method of calculating overtime payments should not, however, be changed. I hope that Mr Taylor will be allowed to present these proposals as this would, I think, greatly increase the chance of their acceptance by the stewards. The increase is being granted in the backing plant because differentials have been altered by the recently introduced incentives in other departments. The shop stewards should therefore understand and accept that the changes in pay structure in the backing plant do not provide any excuses for increases elsewhere in the organization. In particular, the supervisors' representatives might well decide to relate a further claim to the changes in the backing plant. Such a claim on behalf of the supervisors' unions should be rejected totally by management.

Taylor was asked by Lennon to make his proposals at a meeting with backing plant shop stewards. These were immediately accepted, and during the rest of Gray's stay at Tufted there were no further disputes in this section.

Industrial relations—the weekly staff dispute and the Three Day Week

A few days before Christmas the Prime Minister announced the start of the Three Day Week. Characteristically, as soon as Markland heard this news he called a crisis management meeting for 6.0 p.m. that evening. He was clearly very excited by the dramatic prospects of the Three Day Week. On the way to the meeting he encountered Johnson in the corridor. A dazzling smile from Markland prefaced the breathless remark:

'We live in exciting times!'

It was a remark which Johnson was to hear frequently in the months ahead.

The crisis meeting achieved nothing. This was hardly surprising because none of those present had any knowledge of the exact nature of the new restrictions. All that was known was that each factory would only be allowed to use power from the mains on three days of each week. In an attempt to add substance to the meeting Muldoon sent out one of his staff to acquire an evening paper. In declamatory style he read at length to the meeting from this, stopping occasionally to amplify various points which he felt uniquely able to understand. Eventually, in the absence of tangible progress, the managing director adjourned the meeting until first thing the following morning.

In anticipation of events Markland had earlier acquired two diesel generating sets from Holland, and he was very anxious to acquire fuel for these. At that time fuel merchants were restricting the supply of diesel oil to their established customers. Tufted had not previously purchased diesel oil in bulk. At first no one could think of a way to overcome this problem, but eventually Lennon suggested an expedient. All the available lorries were sent out to garages in order to fill their tanks with diesel fuel which, on their return, was transferred to drums. In this way Tufted acquired the fuel to run its generators.

After days of more or less continuous discussion the operating board decided how it was going to face the Three Day Week. After the New Year, each of the three factories would be allowed to draw power from the mains on Mondays, Tuesdays and Wednesdays only. This allocation was something of a blow; it had been hoped that one of the factories would have been allocated Thursdays, Fridays and Saturdays. This would have enabled all the factories to work five full days with the aid of the generators. It was decided that the most likely threat to production would come from a shortage of spun yarn. For this reason one of the generators was placed permanently at the Batley factory. The remaining generator was to be shared between Leeds and Cleckheaton. One week the generator would be in Leeds, allowing it to work for a full seven days, while Cleckheaton worked only three days. The allocation was to be reversed on the following week.

Batley spun only about a quarter of the company's yarn requirement, but provided the deficiency could continue to be met from outside suppliers this strategy looked sound enough to maintain output at the level it would have been had the factories been restricted to the normal five day week. The only further task now was to obtain the agreement of the employees to operate this arrangement. No one on the board expected any difficulties in that direction.

Lennon and Johnson called a meeting of the shop stewards representing the manual workers. These were to receive their normal premiums of 50 per cent and 100 per cent respectively for Saturdays and Sundays, but would not be paid for those periods in which work was not possible. For the moment the agreement which existed on the guaranteed working week was suspended. Clerical staff were to work a normal week, although they could only work during daylight on Thursdays and Fridays. They were not, in general, required at weekends when the factories were working off generators. Some of the monthly staff were asked to attend at weekends, but were allowed to take time off as compensation in periods when power was not available. These proposals were accepted without protest.

The weekly staff were only required on the premises when production was possible, as they supervised the work of the hourly paid. Lennon and Johnson proposed to them that they would receive overtime premiums for Saturday and Sunday working, but would, in common with the hourly paid, not receive payment for those periods when production was not possible. It was suggested to them that they should take these days off in lieu of their normal payments.

These proposals were rejected by this group of employees: they maintained that, as staff, they should be paid for a full week each week—irrespective of whether they had any work to do. In other words, they argued that they should be paid their normal salaries for those weekdays when power was not available.

The first of January, which was a bank holiday, fell on a Tuesday when the factories were allowed to draw power from the mains. The hourly paid had agreed to work on this bank holiday for double time. Those at the Leeds factory were then to be laid off on the Thursday and Friday of that week. The weekly staff at this plant refused the offer of five days pay for this week plus either Thursday or Friday off as compensation for working Tuesday. They demanded to be paid double time for Tuesday and to be paid for Thursday and Friday as well.

Lennon and Johnson felt that the company could not accede to the demand of the weekly staff. Markland had no doubts that the company should stand firm. Gray's advice was sought and he too was of the same opinion. The dispute was put to the local secretary of their union and he advised acceptance of the management offer. However, the weekly staff continued to refuse to accept. When Tuesday came, the factories worked without the first line supervision for that day and this work was performed by the monthly staff. This created much tension between the two grades of staff, and for sometime afterwards the weekly paid threatened to leave the supervisors' union and join another one.

After the refusal of the weekly staff to work on the Tuesday, Johnson drafted a notice to all employees, which Lennon signed. It stated that the factories would not work on weekends because the weekly staff had refused to work 'under conditions consistent with their terms of employment, and endorsed by their union official'. The strategy worked out in the boardroom for maintaining production at a near normal level in spite of the Three Day Week could not be implemented.

It is hardly possible to judge the rights and wrongs of a dispute of this nature. Lennon, Johnson, Markland, and Gray all felt that any concession to the weekly staff might spark off claims among the hourly paid workers. They were also unsure as to whether the output which would have resulted from weekend working would be needed.

The weekly staff felt that it was quite wrong for the monthly staff to obtain their normal salaries, while they were put on much the same basis as the hourly paid. Certainly, the dispute itself brought to the surface a lot of bad feeling which had been building up over a long period. The dispute provided an opportunity for the weekly staff to express their discontent. The cause of that discontent had roots deeper than the issues involved in the immediate dispute.

It should not be assumed that the problems of the staff and the workforce provided a constant, or even, regular topic of conversation at management meetings or in the boardroom generally. In fact, they were hardly mentioned. At the height of the dispute with the weekly staff the topic of industrial relations at Tufted was briefly discussed by the directors over coffee. Tenniswood believed that the trouble was caused by the Welfare State and made worse by the chicanery of the well-known trade union general secretary, whose union was unrepresented at Tufted. Palmer argued forcefully that the company should adopt a hard line and sack all the weekly staff and said pompously:

'It is high time management started reasserting its prerogatives.'

Smith recalled an obscure anecdote about one of his previous employers who had been confronted by a quite different staff problem.

Lennon was involved much more than the other directors in the day-to-day problems of the workforce, but he did not look to them for advice or encouragement. Most of them, in fact, hardly ever set foot inside the factories. They spent most of their time in each others' offices or in the boardroom. Industrial relations were discussed mainly in terms of what had been said about the subject on television. The personalities and public statements of leading trade union figures were regularly discussed by directors in the boardroom, and often with much feeling. Their discussions were usually hostile to the trade unions. They were typified by an exchange in the boardroom between Palmer and Lennon discussing two leading trade unionists. Palmer began by naming one of them and saying:

'He's a Marxist; bastards like that should be shot for treason.'

Lennon liked to demonstrate his superior wisdom and he claimed that the man named was not the real villain.

'He's an honest bastard though.'

He went on to discuss the other trades unionist:

'Now he's the real nigger in the woodpile—he talks all sweet reason when he's on the box, but when he's talking in private, he really is a bastard. That man won't be satisfied until the whole capitalist system comes tumbling down.'

Discussions of the sanctions enacted by the unions at Tufted were carried on in similar cavalier fashion. Palmer would adopt an aggressive stance.

'Give 'em their cards and get 'em off the plot,' was his typical phrase.

Lennon was scarcely more moderate in the boardroom. However, he never related the boardroom discussions to the reality of the shop stewards' meetings which he attended. Apart from himself, it was doubtful whether any of the directors of the company actually knew the names, or even the faces of the shop stewards, and Lennon would not seriously consider acting on their advice.

The management accounts

The problems of the staff and work force had never been included on the agenda of management meetings in the boardroom. Since Markland's arrival these meetings had been devoted almost entirely to an examination of the previous month's management accounts. The system produced both monthly accounts and weekly profit flashes. The former set of documents were very substantial in size and complexity; they weighed on average about half a kilo and contained thousands of entries calculated to the third decimal point of a pound. Gray had instantly come to the conclusion, that the management accounts were a ludicrous exercise in futility. Their sheer size and the pompously phrased analyses which they contained struck him as absurd. It did not require, in his opinion, any analysis to see that the figures in the accounts were utterly phoney and useless. He was rather surprised that the managing director did not seem to embrace this view himself. However, he was not put off by Markland's lack of support; he had never been able to suffer fools gladly, and he continued to express his opinions about the system and Muldoon in most outspoken terms.

The intrinsic futility of the accounts had not been apparent to Johnson on first inspection, but he had quickly come to the same conclusion as Gray, albeit by a more cautious and analytical route. In his representations to Markland, Gray increasingly used arguments and illustrations which were derived from Johnson's analysis of the system.

The system attempted to relate the actual performance of the company against that stipulated by an annual budget. The advisers did not know at this stage that Markland himself had been largely responsible for devising the budget for the financial year 1973–74. The annual budget was sub-divided into months. In each month individual production targets were set for each quality of carpet. These were expressed in terms of square yards. A failure to achieve this stipulated target would result in an 'adverse variance'. If production targets were exceeded then, a 'positive variance' would be recorded. Standards were also set in respect of such things as labour and material costs. If actual expenditure under these headings exceeded that laid down by the pre-determined standards, then, 'adverse variances' were recorded. The opposite was the case if actual expenditure was less than that laid down as standard. In such instances 'positive variances' were recorded.

It was supposed that the company would be in a profit position if positive variances outweighed negative ones. The break-even position was assumed to be attained when the two were in balance. At that point the profit on production was thought to be just sufficient to offset fixed costs such as are represented by plant and machinery. In the event of positive variances exceeding negative ones it would be said that 'overheads were over recovered'. The opposite situation was referred to as the 'under recovery of overheads'. The monthly accounts and the weekly profit flashes purported to show whether overheads were being under or over recovered and, therefore, whether profits were being made or not.

The system was also supposed to highlight the features in the organization which were contributing to success or failure. The existence of negative variances was, for example, supposed to alert management's attention to the weaknesses in the organization which were responsible for losses. It was assumed, for example, that a certain percentage of material wastage was allowable for the whole range of output. This percentage was held to be constant regardless of changes in the volume and composition of production. Let it be supposed that the recorded material wastage was greater than that stipulated as

78

standard. In this case a negative variance would, in theory, suggest to management that corrective action should be taken. It might be discovered that material wastage was unusually high because certain machines were used to produce carpet for which they were not ideally suited. However, it might also be discovered that this could hardly have been avoided if certain orders were to be completed within a given time. This situation might not arise again because the demand for that particular carpet could even out. Again, it might be found that an unusually high level of material wastage was associated with some defective consignments of yarn or other materials. The next consignments might be of superior quality. Even if the system had been monitored in this way, the results would have been almost worthless because of the very nature of the interaction between sales and production. Post-mortems of this kind would be very expensive to conduct and would not necessarily provide guides to future action.

Johnson was especially struck by the excessive importance which the accounts attached to a relatively small item of cost-labour. Labour, on average, accounted for about 9p of the cost involved in producing a square yard of carpet. This particular cost was analysed under six different headings. At least two-thirds of the accounting effort was devoted to the analysis of labour costs. Relatively little attention was devoted to material costs which varied from about 60p to £2.50 per square yard. The relative neglect of material costs seemed to be particularly absurd to him because, at that time, the prices of fibre and other materials were rising fast.

The system embodied two important assumptions. The first of these consisted in the belief that profit margins were higher on those carpets which had more value added to the costs of material in the course of production. This bias was built into the system with the result that Markland believed that the accounts demonstrated empirically that the company would be better off if it concentrated production on the more expensive ranges of carpet. The production standards embodied in the budget were set mostly in the product design stage. These consistently underestimated actual material wastage on the more expensive ranges of carpet. This was understandable because realistic estimates would have indicated that most of the work of the design department was commercially misconceived. As a result of this in-built bias Markland had drawn the inference from the accounts that Tufted should move 'up-market'.

The second assumption built into the system was that the degree of plant utilization was of paramount importance in achieving profitability. The whole boardroom had come to believe that the key to salvation lay in producing more and more square yards. Johnson appreciated that the attempt to maximize production in quantitative terms led to higher rates of material wastage and increased the proportion of sub-standard carpet made. He also saw that most of the machinery in the factories was designed for mass production, but the more expensive ranges could not be sold in the requisite quantities and it seemed evident to him that the assumptions in the accounting system were self-contradictory. Indeed, it was perfectly obvious that the policy of moving up-market was inconsistent with that which indicated that profit depended crucially upon square yardage.

Leyland agreed with Johnson's analysis and added further doubts. He thought many of the standards embodied in the accounts were entirely arbitrary. He knew that the data on stock levels and other items which were fed into the accounts were hopelessly in error. It was evident to them both that the accounts were also full of computational errors. They too, like Gray, began to be puzzled by Markland's reluctance to admit these sort of things. Indeed, at management meetings he continued to treat the accounts with the utmost seriousness.

Johnson and Leyland began to mock the terminology of the accounts whenever possible, substituting 'adverse variance' for the shortage of anything from sugar in the morning coffee to good television programmes recalled from the previous evening. The particular phrase which caught their imagination was, however, 'the under recovery of overheads'. When Markland and Muldoon were both present in the boardroom, they would solicitously ask the latter whether he had 'over recovered his dunderheads' or ask him if his abstention from sugar in coffee was an attempt to 'over recover his waist line'.

Gray made direct and private representations to Markland. He asked him how, and by whom, the budgets had been set. He received an evasive reply. Early in January he made the following observation to Markland:

'I don't just see why the budgeted sales are thought to be better than actual sales. What the hell are we supposed to do with "mix variances". They're bound to happen, it's inevitable that actual sales will differ from the budget. We don't even make all of the bloody styles that are in the budget.'

Verbal representations of this kind seemed not to be making the impact that Gray had hoped for, so he began to write to the managing director about the subject. For instance on 16 January, he wrote:

▶ I should mention my growing doubts about the system of management accounts adopted at Tufted. I understand that the system was designed and installed by a firm of management consultants. It seems to me to be a perfectly standard system, suitable perhaps, for an engineering firm engaged on small batch production; it has little, if any relevance to operations at Tufted. The system encourages the belief that notional profit margins on various kinds of carpet and yardage are matters of supreme importance. It also enables many people to go round the factory talking as though plant utilization should assume a high priority. The plain truth is that material costs represent something like 60 to 70 per cent of total cost.

The letter went on to attack other features of the system, and after listing several weaknesses it concluded:

▶ The present management accounting system enshrines these, and other absurdities in a mass of meaningless statistics and jargon. The trouble is that these seem to be taken seriously and are produced at the cost of a great deal of computer- and man-time.

After receiving this letter Markland said to him:

'You keep on running the system down, but you don't suggest anything better to put in it's place.'

'How can I do that. I'm not an accountant and I've not got the time.'

'I agree. You've got neither the ability nor the energy to design a better system.'

'All right, but can't you see that it's useless and we'd be much better off without it.'

'You're just negative. How do you think I can hope to run a business like this without management accounting?'

'Well, just tell me something. Where on earth do all those budget figures come from? Who decided on them? They seem entirely arbitrary to me.'

'Somewhere or other there's a book which explains it all.'

'Who's got it?'

'Muldoon, I think.'

Gray's feelings about the system were based on an intuition which had been confirmed by Johnson's and Leyland's analyses. However, in the face of the managing director's unbending attitude, he found it difficult to argue that all such systems must necessarily be self-defeating.

The resident directors were not, with the possible exception of Palmer, active supporters of the management accounting system. So far as they were concerned it was innocuous. The existence of adverse variances did not of itself mean that particular directors were taken to task. For example, the management accounts for December 1973 showed an 'adverse usage variance' of 21.5 per cent under the budget heading of 'dyes and chemicals'. This implied that there had been a certain amount of mismanagement in the dyehouse. Markland asked Lennon about this as the dyehouse came within his area of jurisdiction. The latter mumbled something and confessed that he was rather confused as to what exactly the accounts referred. Muldoon intervened anxiously, to explain at great length the precise meaning of this entry. After this exposition everyone became too confused to remember the origin of the discussion. The directors as a whole reacted to the accounts with a mixture of incomprehension and inertia. They did not openly attack the basis of the accounting system itself, as that would be considered as an intrusion into the commercial manager's territory. They had no desire to do this, so long as the accounts were not used as an excuse for interference in their territories. Markland's outbursts based upon the accounts were, they realized, empty rhetorical gestures.

Muldoon's department was largely sustained by the demands which the system made. Large quantities of data had to be collected and processed. The feverish activity required to gather and present enormous amounts of data with the approach of monthly deadlines became the *raison d'être* of the department. The resident directors intuitively assessed the system in political terms. At no time did they ever imagine that it was, operationally speaking, of any use whatsoever. They entirely agreed with Gray's strictures, but unlike him, they could not see any political point in making a protest.

According to conventional theory the main purpose of management accounting is to highlight the weaknesses within organizations so that corrective action can be taken. If these weaknesses were real so that specific and concrete remedies could be taken, then, the system itself would run counter to the conventions of the boardroom. The management accounting system was accepted by the resident directors at Tufted because they correctly perceived it as politically innocuous.

Johnson, Leyland, and Gray, however, could claim to have won at least one minor victory. Markland's discussions of the monthly accounts were becoming much less protracted. What he and Muldoon said about the accounts began to lose even an outward credibility.

Markland and job specifications
Markland had a great deal of enthusiasm for formal job specifications and within a few days of his arrival at Tufted he wrote to members of the operating board asking them for their version of their own job

specifications, he particularly asked that they delineate their responsibilities, authority, and limitations. Smith, alone among the directors, refused to be drawn into answering these specific points. He sent the following memorandum to Markland:

▶ re: Job Specification

I have never been given a job specification and my appointment was confirmed with a shake of the hand, which was quite sufficient so far as I was concerned. We did not discuss the job in any particular detail, but I have always understood it to be to ensure that the maximum amount of carpet is sold at the best possible price.

There were no limitations mentioned and I have always tried to perform the above mentioned duties within the framework and policy of the company, as it applied at the time.

I have naturally no objection to a job specification and will be pleased to discuss this with you at any time.

Markland was furious when he received this reply. Smith's high salary and substantial expense account already rankled him greatly. He saw that this letter quietly mocked his style of management with its emphasis on techniques and rhetoric.

Muldoon's reply was altogether more in line with his expectations. By conventional standards it was easily the most impressive of the specifications submitted. It covered five typescript pages of foolscap. Appended to these were a further four pages which outlined the job of his principal assistant, the data processing manager.

In its preamble Muldoon described his own job under five main headings. These were elaborated by half a page of notes.

The next section was entitled 'Duties'. Under the sub-heading 'Men' were twelve eccentrically numbered paragraphs. For some unexplained reason special importance was attached to the following items:

▶ 12. Ensure that departmental heads run their sections in accordance with company regulations. . . .
20. To be available to all staff for consultation on personal problems.

The next section was called 'Equipment'. It contained four introductory paragraphs numbered 4, 5, 6, and 15. Further sub-sections followed which were headed 'Methods', 'Money', and 'Management'. Each of these sub-sections contained several idiosyncratically numbered paragraphs. Appended to these was an organizational chart which depicted five distinct layers of authority within his department.

This job specification concluded with the enigmatic heading— 'Organization two years hence'. Its sole entry read:

83

► Delete machine accounting, augment computer as per consultant's report.

Smith's rejoinder had been a model of relevance and conciseness. Muldoon's was typical of an administrator, whose job consists largely in generating substantial amounts of meaningless paperwork.

Markland issued Gray with a job specification on 12 December 1973. He believed that Gray was not doing the job for which he was paid. Rather than confront him with this unpleasant news directly, he chose instead to delineate his duties as follows:

► Mr George Gray has been retained by the company as a consultant to advise on industrial relations and future company industrial relations policy.

His main tasks are to consider the following areas:
(a) Information required in the industrial relations field, and methods of presenting that information.
(b) Allocation of responsibilities for total company industrial relations and the splitting up of responsibilities between individual line managers.
(c) Company/union procedures and processes for negotiations, representation, and communication.
(d) Phase Three and its impact on 1974/75 company/union wage negotiations.

Mr Gray is accountable solely to the managing director. He has freedom of contact and communication throughout the company's three plants, but serves in a staff capacity.

This specification was circulated to the operating board. Gray was aware that Markland would have liked him to draw up complicated allocations of responsibility. He was also aware that the managing director attached considerable importance to the work of drawing up elaborate procedures and rules for the conduct of negotiations. This work, however, was in his estimation much less important than the acquisition of some understanding about the causes of the disputes then taking place at Tufted. Although there was very little paperwork to show that Gray had been working, he had even within the first couple of months of his appointment been instrumental in settling disputes which had disrupted production at Tufted. Markland had some appreciation of this, but in his mind the work of managers and consultants could only be affirmed through the production of lengthy reports. He produced these for the chairman himself and he expected Gray to do likewise for him.

Gray had the vague feeling that the memorandum was a command for him to desist from his enquiries into the accounting system and other matters only indirectly related to industrial relations. He was puzzled by the expression 'serves in a staff capacity'. If this meant that he should not himself play an active part in negotiations then, it was not at the time appreciated by him.

Johnson and Leyland undertake a job specification exercise

After Johnson and Leyland had been with the company for a few weeks they received a memorandum from Markland which read:

▶ Could you start to get your thinking caps on re: job specifications for the production director, sales director, marketing director, buying and production control director, and the spinning director; also for Mr Muldoon, the commercial manager.

The specification need not be totally comprehensive but should be a starting point from which we can develop specification authorities and limits of authorities, responsibilities, etc., for management further down the line.

Attached are current ideas on the subject by the parties concerned.

The two of them decided that there was no point in asking the members of the operating board to submit a further description of their own jobs. Johnson suggested that as a first step a form should be circularized to all monthly staff, which invited them to say what they thought their jobs entailed. It contained the following headings—'Title; Responsibility; Main functions; Who reports to you?; What are the main limitations that affect your ability to do your job effectively?'

Markland agreed, and within a week their desks were covered with replies.

Ten forms were returned from the accounts section and these revealed the presence of five chartered accountants. In spite of, or perhaps because of, Muldoon's preoccupation with rules and regulations the replies revealed great confusion within his department. The only financial accountant in the department wrote:

▶ The history of change which has taken place at Tufted over the past two years has involved so many variations in the routines that one cannot always get a clear and concise picture of the work pattern.

A management accountant commented:

▶ The lack of company rules and regulations on methods of payment makes the analysis of the payroll almost impossible.

He also complained that his activities took:

▶ 128 per cent of my time, i.e., an average of 46½ hours per week.

Confusion was also evident in the forms returned from the production departments. Johnson and Leyland were astonished to find that so many managers were scattered around the factories. Cuthbertson, the Leeds factory manager, had two manufacturing departments—the dyehouse and the backing plant. These departments were at the end of the production process, and they received part finished carpet from Cleckheaton. They processed this roughly in the sequence it arrived. Despite the simplicity and predictability of this arrangement, Cuthbertson reported that he spent 70 per cent of his time on 'planning, interpretation, and co-ordination of weekly/daily production requirements'. He complained about 'a lack of information' and also 'apparent confusion in higher management'. Responsible to him was a manager with the title 'manufacturing controller' who complained of 'the lack of definite policy directions' and 'the apparent unwillingness by director level to allow managers to manage'.

The backing plant and dyehouse managers both reported to the controller. They complained about the lack of information and the absence of policy regarding the development of their departments. They also expressed their concern at the lack of a salary differential between themselves and the weekly staff. The dyehouse manager wrote of a 'lack of concern over the physical state of the department'. This was a reference to the dangerous state of the roof.

The assistant dyehouse manager was especially forthright.

▶ The senior management at Tufted must be described as very poor, and often so inept in planning consultation and decision that they often cause more problems than if nothing at all had been done. The lack of facts supplied to departments is disgraceful, especially in respect of financial affairs.

He concluded:

▶ All employees (even the shop floor) should be more fully informed . . . having to apologize to the shop floor for blunder after blunder erodes the staff position.

Johnson and Leyland were surprised not only by the number of managers at Tufted but also by the deep antagonism which many of them expressed towards the company. The idea that anything useful could be achieved by drawing up detailed and formal job specifications struck them as completely absurd. Much of the conflict revealed by the forms stemmed, in their estimation, from gross overstaffing; it was, they thought, a clear case of the broth being spoilt by too many cooks.

Gray had been asserting for some time that the interests of efficiency would be served by substantial reductions in managerial and technical staff. Their survey seemed, to them, to provide incontrovertible evidence in support of this contention.

The only idea which Markland seemed to embrace with real enthusiasm, was a suggestion which Gray made in a letter early in January. The relevant passage read as follows:

▶ In fact there is, in my view, much overstaffing in the categories covered by the supervisors' union as also at the more senior managerial levels. For instance, one of the problems on the industrial relations side is overlapping responsibilities in management. In this case one feels it is partly due to too many managers attempting to do the same job. Again, might I mention the fact that the warehouse is packed, in spite of the company's difficulty in keeping up with recent and current demand. If this is so, something seems radically wrong with marketing and/or production control. I feel sure that overstaffing is contributing to confusion.

In my opinion this is an opportune time—because of the need to economize on fixed costs in short-time working—for the company to review manpower requirements on the managerial and technical levels.

When Gray next visited Markland in his office he was greeted most warmly. Markland jumped out of his chair and pranced around the room repeating over and over again:
'I like it, I like it; overstaffing, overstaffing. I like it, I like it.'

Miscellaneous
Gray persisted, with the support of Johnson and Leyland, in advising the managing director to get rid of both Muldoon and Palmer. He also drew his attention to other problems. For example, he mentioned both verbally and in letters that production and sales seemed to be poorly co-ordinated and went so far as contending that this was the most serious long-term problem at Tufted. Gray and his allies had been too busy on other things to analyse the root causes of this lack of co-ordination, but to all of them it was evident.

They had noticed, for instance, that large quantities of carpet were made only to be put into storage at a time, when customers were continually complaining about long delivery times. Some orders were even refused when large quantities of carpet were being made speculatively. All this seemed to them nonsensical. They believed that the product range should be drastically reduced. Production and sales effort should, they thought, be concentrated on the best selling lines. These were in the lower end of the market. They were, therefore, urging Markland to reverse the sales policy which he had formulated as a result of his examination of the management accounts. They also strongly campaigned to prevent him signing a contract for a new computer, so that the scope of the management accounting system could be extended. In spite of this advice Markland, in the end, committed himself to the contract.

10
The origins of action

A state of emergency

Towards the end of 1973 the national news was dominated by a dispute in the mining industry. Stocks of coal at power stations were, as a result, reduced to a dangerously low level. In November the Government introduced emergency regulations in an attempt to reduce the consumption of electricity. Later, in December, it took the drastic step of putting the whole of manufacturing industry onto a three day week so as to reduce the consumption of electricity still further.

At Tufted, Muldoon took it upon himself to enforce the emergency regulations. He promptly circularized his colleagues informing them of what was, and what was not, permitted. The electricians followed their instructions scrupulously. They removed the fuses from all the space heaters. Even the one in Markland's office was subjected to this indignity. The implied impartiality of this treatment was negated by the fact that he was provided with a large and efficient butane gas fire. Other directors and managers were allocated oil heaters whose proficiency and capacity were proportionate to their rank. Johnson and Leyland arrived after this allocation had been made, and they had to be content with the meanest and smelliest of the available heaters.

Markland's office was, thanks to the butane fire, kept comfortably warm. The remaining offices varied from rather chilly to bitterly cold. An energetic Muldoon also supervised the enforcement of the regulations which restricted the amount of electricity used to light offices. Except for an hour or two at midday, the dimness of the offices was such that routine clerical work demanded something akin to the Dunkirk spirit.

Outside the factories, the streets were barely illuminated, and some were completely unlit. Overnight the bright lights of an industrialized civilization were extinguished by decree; the whole country was plunged into a medieval darkness.

These circumstances undoubtedly affected Johnson's and Leyland's early impressions of Tufted. The cold and gloom of their offices meant that they spent much less time in them than would otherwise have been the case. In their search for an odd corner of warmth they enlarged the circle of their acquaintances. At times they resorted to brisk walks around the factories in order to restore their flagging circulations. These excursions presented them with impressions of Tufted which were quite different to those pictured in the management accounts.

The emergency regulations and the Three Day Week provided an opportunity for action which was lacking in more normal times. At Tufted, suggestions were taken seriously which a few weeks earlier would have been laughed out of court.

Johnson and Leyland's situation

Johnson and Leyland reported directly to Markland. The fact that they were not attached to any particular department presented them with a challenge. Normally, the time of an executive is more or less fully taken up by the routine paperwork and ritualized interactions which are in-built features of departmental life. In their early weeks at Tufted Markland had hardly given any indication of what he expected of them. He had implied in their job specifications that they were to interest themselves in Lennon and Tenniswood's areas respectively. He had also handed Johnson a dossier containing some management accounts.

Johnson did not find this lack of initial guidance much of a problem. He had spent years as a consultant arriving at companies which were strange to him, and he had become very proficient at generating, under these circumstances, large amounts of paperwork which purported to describe operations. Only on the rarest occasions had any director queried his flow charts and descriptions of shop floor systems. He had learned that most directors had only the vaguest ideas about the production processes employed in their own factories. At Tufted he reverted to the pattern of behaviour which he had acquired as a consultant. He did, incidentally, acquire by this behaviour a rudimentary knowledge of the manufacturing process at Tufted. Certainly, some of the members of the operating board, including Markland himself, lacked this advantage. Johnson kept a careful record of this early work just in case Markland should enquire about how he was spending his time. Included in this record was the following description of the manufacturing process:

▶ Yarn is bought ready-wound on the required number of bobbins. Each bobbin feeds a single line of tufts. The broadloom tufting machines have 1000 to 1500 separate lines of tufts and hence the large construction (the creel) is needed to mount the bobbins. The tufting machine has a row of needles across the width of the carpet being made. Each needle is threaded with its own yarn from its own bobbin. Backing material is bought in rolls, slightly wider than the required finished product. It is fed through the line of needles; each needle produces a tuft; and the backing cloth is advanced a fraction of an inch for the next row of tufts to be inserted.

Some 200 feet of partly finished carpet is produced as a 'double roll'. This is the amount that can be readily handled. It must then be fed through a large machine called a 'backing plant'. A thin layer of latex is deposited on the undersurface of the backing material in order to anchor the tufts. A second layer may be foam or it may be a second hessian material. Its function is to cover the latex. When the foam backing is applied, the carpet does not require an underlay. Backed carpet is trimmed to a constant width, and is cut to a manageable length; usually about 100 ft at a time. Such a length is known as a 'full roll' of carpet.

We have several variations to the basic manufacturing process. Some tufting machines alter the size of tuft produced by each needle, a very small tuft is 'buried' by its two neighbours which are made comparatively large. This produces a patterned carpet even though the yarn on any single column of tufts is invariably the same colour. These are the 'scroll' machines, which cost more and operate more slowly, than the standard machines. Some tufting machines only produce a looped pile, others can make a 'cut pile'. Shearing is used to cut off the tops of high loops and leave low loops uncut, to make a 'cut and loop' carpet. We have a machine on order which can make 'cut and loop' carpets without an ancillary operation.

Many creels of yarn are bought ready dyed to their final colour. Some, particularly nylon yarns, are bought in an 'undyed' state. The subsequent carpet can be dyed complete, in the dye-house before backing. Some of these creels have alternate yarns that take up dye to a different extent and come out of the dyeing operation as two different colours. This makes simple patterned carpets. We are also starting to make printed carpets. The pattern is applied to a plain tufted carpet and we can make carpets that look like Axminster woven carpets. This is done on partly finished carpet, and backing is usually the final operation.

Full rolls of carpet from the backing plant are inspected on special frames, and then are sent to the warehouse. If a customer buys full rolls of carpet, they are dispatched direct from the warehouse; when he buys a specific length, it is sent to the cutting room where the length is cut off. The rest of the roll is held in the cutting room for future orders, or if it is too short, it is sent to 'remnants' to be sold off.

Leyland found the absence of routine work more embarrassing. He lacked Johnson's varied experience and was much less used to working entirely on his own. His problem was compounded by the fact that Tenniswood, unlike Lennon, was not readily approachable. He could never be sure when Markland would burst unannounced into his office. This circumstance obliged him to maintain a posture of readiness with pencil in hand. The strain this caused provided him with a reason to leave his office and seek out the company of Johnson.

Markland at this time adopted the stance of a man of action and gave every appearance of supreme confidence. The two executives automatically assumed that he wanted them to provide him with an analysis of the problems at Tufted and a programme of action to combat them. Their freedom from routine tasks enabled them to undertake this analysis, but they could not act—they could only advise. They looked to Markland to implement their ideas. If he had acted upon their advice more decisively they would have felt reassured.

It is important not to exaggerate their sense of insecurity. When an executive first joins an organization he goes through a sort of honeymoon period. His own perceptions of the new company tend to be rather rose-tinted, and many of the established employees try to play fair with him by giving him the benefit of the doubt. Johnson and Leyland did go through such a honeymoon period at Tufted. However, none of the resident directors took them into their confidence. After all, they were at this stage more concerned to take the measure of Markland himself. These circumstances made the two new executives very dependent on the managing director. Their commitment to action resulted mainly from the fact that they tended to take him at face value during their honeymoon period. The truth was that Markland had by his rhetoric deceived himself as well as them. He genuinely convinced himself that he was a man of action, and he did this by mistaking words for deeds. Johnson and Leyland did not make that particular mistake but, at first, they failed to see that Markland was making it. This failure on their part led them into the kind of over-extended commitment to ideas and persons which politically shrewd executives instinctively avoid.

After a month or more they began to appreciate, uncertainly at first, the fact that Markland was reluctant to translate proposals into action. Of the two, Johnson was the bolder. By the end of January he was taunting him with the remark—'rattle rattle'—whenever the managing director started to engage in histrionics. He implied by these words that Markland was content to make clanking sounds with his sabre instead of putting it to active use.

Gray's situation

Gray was less deeply involved than either of the two executives in his commitment to Tufted. This was inevitable because his consultancy was only incidental to his main work at the business school. However, he was not devoid of commitment, although he went to great pains to hide this. The rather donnish exterior which he adopted was a defence mechanism which he used to conceal the strength of his emotions and his attachments. From the start he felt a strong loyalty toward Markland. He also felt guilty about receiving his fees and some very generous expenses without giving something in return. With the passage of time he also became genuinely interested in the problems at Tufted. He developed a commitment to solve these in order to satisfy his intellectual curiosity. Again, with the passage of time he became more committed to serving the interests of his allies, Johnson and Leyland. He became increasingly angry with his patron because of his failure to commit himself wholeheartedly to action. In private Gray became very outspoken to Markland. He called him 'an empty windbag', more than once. On one occasion he said:

'It's useless for you to make warlike noises if you don't intend to act. The directors will think that you're all bark and no bite. You'll undermine your own credibility if you carry on in this way. If you don't intend to do anything it would be much better to say nothing.'

On a more mundane level Gray also had problems. Markland had not thought it necessary to allocate him an office. He was therefore forced to spend his time in other people's offices, or on the shop floor. Although this helped him to understand what went on at Tufted it detracted from his status in the eyes of others, particularly in those of the resident directors. Markland had not made the slightest attempt to announce his arrival with a flourish or fanfare. It may have been that Markland did not go to pains to signal Gray's status because he considered that the resident directors were not worth the effort which this would have involved. Certainly, the consultant's importance and status would have been confirmed if he had allocated him one of the larger offices.

The fact that Gray did not insist on this sort of thing reflected his lack of experience as a professional consultant. He had done odd bits of consultancy, but most of his recent experience in industry had been in a research capacity. He always started by asking himself the question: What is going on here? He had found out that flaunting his own status made it difficult, or even impossible, for him to obtain answers to this question. Although he was now a consultant, he continued to behave as though he was a researcher.

If Gray had been more experienced, he would have insisted that an office was allocated to him. In the absence of an office an experienced consultant would have sought to advertise his presence in spectacular ways. For instance, he might have thought of encamping himself in the boardroom itself. Such an idea did not occur to Gray.

Professional consultants are taught to arrive at the client's premises first thing in the morning. They will spend a lot of time and money dressing in the correct image. They are obsessive users of deodorants and make frequent visits to the more expensive kind of gentlemen's hairdresser. They will appear to have little time to spare for coffee or lunch. At all times they will appear to be anxious to turn the conversation towards business topics, and to give the impression that the whole of their time and energy is devoted to the job in hand. They will adopt a thoughtful posture when sitting in their offices and they are never seen without a pencil at the ready. They habitually adopt some of the subtler forms of ingratiation. For instance, they will always preface their remarks to the managing director with some kind of apology for disturbing his work. At the end of a hard day devoted to image projection, they will be seen to be working when the client's employees are going home. They will acquire the habit of telephoning the managing director frequently during the early part of the evening to establish the fact that they, at least, are still working. They are taught that their main job is to provide written reports which will provide firm evidence of their application after they have gone. They are taught that it is relatively unimportant or even undesirable to attempt to improve the client's operations in any way. Therefore, they usually spend up to eighty per cent of their time drafting and re-drafting reports to ensure that the right impression is created. The actions proposed must, if possible, be innocuous and non-controversial. At all times professional consultants must behave as though they were guests. Under no circumstances must they offend even the meanest member of the boardroom.

Gray embodied very few, if any, of these characteristics. His appearance was unconventional, and he did not devote any energy to promoting the requisite professional image. He was frequently late in arriving, and before he turned his attention to business matters, he would claim his expenses from Markland's secretary and then enjoy a leisurely cup of coffee in the boardroom. He had an undisguised contempt for written reports and was not afraid of letting his opinions be known even when these ran counter to the prejudices of the directors.

He was not deliberately flaunting the conventional standards of the professional consultant. He had not considered the possibility that he should adapt his behaviour to suit this norm; he was trying to influence the conduct of industrial relations at Tufted. He believed that he could not do this by burying himself in an office and by periodically charging down corridors with a piece of paper in hand. However, he found the task of making contact with strangers on the shop floor emotionally exhausting, and there were times when he felt the need for a private office of his own so that he could put his feet up for half an hour or so. He was perplexed by Markland's failure to provide him with such accommodation, and by the fact that he had not heralded his arrival and underlined his status to the resident directors. His quandary was that he was unable to reconcile Markland's private commitment and encouragement with his lack of publicly advertised support. He was a stranger in a slightly hostile environment, unsure of what was required of him.

He became committed to action for reasons that he did not quite understand. In part, action seemed to him to be an escape from the ambiguities of his situation; it seemed to be a way of clearing the air. He was not taken in, to the same extent, by Markland's front as were Johnson and Leyland. He had known Markland under different circumstances. Even so, he did not in his first months at Tufted by any means fully appreciate the extent to which he and Markland habitually conversed on different levels.

Resort to theatricality

Suddenly, and apparently on the spur of the moment, Markland announced his intention to hold a weekend conference of the operating board. A day or two before it was due to start, Leyland said to Gray:

'Surely, George, we now know enough to act? If ever there was a moment to act decisively it must be now. Why does David hold back like this? Why does he go through the charade of calling this stupid conference?'

'Yes, of course, we know enough to act. You're absolutely right. I can't understand David either. Perhaps he will act. Perhaps this is his way of doing it. I'd take the bull by the horns if I were him. I've not had a chance to see him. He asks our advice—seems to agree, but then does things like this!'

Neither of them, nor for that matter Johnson, had the faintest idea at that stage of just how committed Markland was both to Muldoon and to Palmer. They did not know that the managing director himself had elevated Muldoon to operating board status. Nor did they know about the close association with Palmer which he had formed on his earlier visits to Tufted. He had not confided to them that he was the mysterious unknown person who had devised the budget targets used in the management accounts.

They could not understand his reluctance to act against Muldoon and Palmer, nor why he had continued to use the management accounts as an agenda for the operating board. He could not offer a single counter argument to their criticisms of the accounting system other than the suggestion that they should work on designing a better one. In spite of this, he contrived to give all three of his advisers the impression that he would act along the general lines which they were indicating. He gave them the further impression that he was waiting so as to strike the first blows at the most opportune time.

When Markland felt confronted by problems which he could not understand he habitually resorted to theatricality. It had, after all, worked very well for him in the past. The very fact he chose this moment to appeal to the operating board meant that action based logically on the investigation undertaken by his advisers was ruled out.

The operating board could not be expected to agree, for instance, to the complete shut down of Muldoon's management accounting section and Palmer's department. These departmental heads would, of course, oppose bitterly such a suggestion, and it would be a contravention of boardroom conventions for other directors to support wholesale measures of this kind. They might support all-round, but commensurate, reductions in staff because such a course would not infringe upon their relative territories.

The only staff department which could be virtually eliminated with the concurrence of the operating board as a whole was management services. The head of this department was not on the operating board and reported directly to the managing director. The elimination of this department would not therefore be seen as a direct threat by any of the resident directors.

Markland by referring problems to the operating board also effectively deferred any immediate and decisive action against some of its members. Why take someone's advice when one intends to dismiss him forthwith? The resort to theatricality was Markland's way of achieving some sort of compromise between old and new allegiances. Such a posture was incompatible with any consistent programme of action.

11

The four orders: a digression

Introduction

Gray's criticisms of the management accounting system were specific. Markland rebutted these by asking him to suggest either improvements in its design or, alternatively, a better system. The consultant did not have a theory to support his intuition that all such systems must be ineffectual.

When Markland said to him:

'It's quite unthinkable to attempt to manage a place like this without a system of management accounting', he was expressing an opinion backed up by the whole weight of orthodox theory. All Gray could say in reply was that this theory was mistaken and make the point that if a system was not working then one might as well be without it. He lacked a theory which would have enabled him to make a frontal attack on Markland's preconceptions.

The germs of such a theory were starting to form in Johnson's mind, even as early as the beginning of January 1974. He began to describe management services, personnel, marketing, and management accounting as 'the abstract departments'. This description implied that the work of these departments had little, if any, practical relevance to the primary task of making and selling carpet. This lack of relevance was, he believed, due to the non-empirical outlook of most of the staff in these departments. It seemed to him as though these staff spent their time elaborating abstractions and applying routines which were entirely lacking in practicality.

These early thoughts eventually promoted the development of the theory of the four orders. This theory owes much to hindsight—something which although despised must, nevertheless, be used if one is to learn from experience. Consequently, the theory stands slightly apart from the chronicle of events described in this book. It is added in order to bring out more clearly the reasons for, and the implications of, the lack of connection which so often seems to exist between the work of staff departments and the accomplishment of primary tasks. And, if there are still any Johnsons, Leylands, and Grays beavering around in industry they will, the writers believe, welcome the ammunition provided by the four orders.

First order operations and administration

The primary task of a manufacturing company is to make and sell its products. First order operations are those which are essential to the accomplishment of primary tasks. The manufacturing processes at Tufted obviously came within this category. It was also obvious that the dispatch and delivery of carpet to customers was an indispensable operation. Likewise, it was essential to maintain machinery, vehicles, and the plant itself because sooner or later their neglect would make it impossible to manufacture or distribute carpet.

The primary task also necessitated various administrative activities. For instance, production could not have been maintained for long unless orders for yarn, backing cloth, foam, and other materials were placed with suppliers. Again, transactions demanded that customers be invoiced and sales ledgers kept. Employees would not work without payment. Consequently, it was essential to calculate pay slips and see that arrangements were made to fill pay packets with requisite amounts of money. Businesses are required by law to present balance sheets and make tax returns. This necessitates certain records and bookkeeping. All these activities are essential to the accomplishment of the primary task and they will therefore be classified under the heading of 'first order administration'.

The work involved in securing loans to cover short-term losses or temporary shortages of liquidity is often crucial to the survival of a company. In the longer term, the work involved in raising funds to finance investment for new plant and machinery can be equally indispensable. One of the problems at Tufted was created by the fact that much of this first order administration was undertaken on its behalf by staff employed at Total's head office. This physical separation of the administrator from the reality which he is meant to control does create difficulties. It can, and did, happen that staff at headquarters made operational decisions purely on the basis of formal information. Quite often this information was misleading and administrators were, because of their location, unable to check it by on the spot inspections.

It is difficult or even impossible to imagine how an organization like Tufted could operate without at least a rudimentary structure of authority. Indeed, such an organization is by definition such a structure. For this reason supervision at Tufted was an integral part of first order administration.

First order operations, whether administrative or otherwise, can be discharged with varying degrees of efficiency and economy, but the fact that they can be performed wastefully should not be allowed to obscure their essential character.

A first order organization is, so far as day-to-day tasks are concerned, largely or wholly self co-ordinating. The work of everyone is by definition essential, and provided always that excessive overstaffing is avoided the contribution that an individual makes will be missed in his absence. If appropriate raw materials are not purchased in requisite amounts at suitable times, then production and sales will be adversely affected. Those who perform these latter tasks will, in such circumstances, pressurize buyers. If these fail to respond to this stimulation, then others will combine to secure their removal or transfer. Elaborate management control systems are not required when the work of everyone is both essential and interdependent.

Overstaffing in the first order

Overmanning and low effort standards are frequently a feature of first order operations. The design of machinery and plant is such as to impose fairly obvious limits on the number of men it is feasible to employ on physical tasks. Matters are rather different in administrative contexts. Here, the abstractness or intangibility of many of the tasks make it more difficult to determine the number of men needed, and the time necessary for their accomplishment. Overstaffing is more pervasive than overmanning even though it is usually less evident visually.

At Tufted, years of empire building had created layer upon layer of authority within the management structure. For example, six gradations interposed themselves between an operator in the backing plant and the managing director. These were: chargehand, shift foreman, backing plant manager, manufacturing controller, works manager, and production director. The work of the sales force was clearly a first order activity, but here too there was much overstaffing. Accretion had created four layers of authority between an ordinary salesman and the director of home sales. These were sales-force manager, area manager, regional manager, and general sales manager.

Overstaffing of this magnitude impairs the performance of essential work; it creates conflict and indecision. All the managers in the long chains of command were underemployed, but the ethos at Tufted did not allow them to advertise their enforced idleness. They felt obliged to conceal this by creating unnecessary work. For instance, they would invent paperwork both for their subordinates and themselves. This caused much frustration, and it served to divert attention and effort away from relevant tasks. For want of anything better to do, managers would spend much of their time in evaluating and pressurizing their subordinates. Naturally, this was resented and subordinates would react either with open hostility or by resorting to various forms of calculated inefficiency. Overstaffing also manifested itself in the frequency and regularity of office conferences. The slightest pretext was sufficient to justify a meeting, and often they took place only because they had been scheduled. Frequently, these gatherings were unable to resolve even trivial questions because of personal rivalries among managers. Internecine activity of this kind helped to absorb spare time, and it also served as a channel for the expression of frustration caused by the fact that it was often next to impossible to get even the simplest thing done. The indecision and conflict caused by excessive overstaffing detracts from the effective performance of essential operations.

Second order administration

The outstanding characteristic of the second order administrator is that he seeks to apply what are thought to be well attested ideas and techniques to organizations. These ideas and techniques are grounded in abstractions. The second order administrator applies what is often regarded as a body of scientifically verified knowledge. Thus, for example, management accounting is thought to consist of rigorously worked out concepts and procedures. A management accountant is thought to possess knowledge which is readily transferable from one organization to another. The second order administrator does not derive his procedures from empirical analysis of first order operations. He applies the procedures that he has been taught and which are amplified in conventional textbooks. These procedures he superimposes on organizations with little, if any, regard to their empirical characteristics. The second order administrator dislikes and rejects empiricism and common sense.

Second order administration has its origin in overstaffing within the first order. At Tufted, for instance, the manager of the Leeds factory had the leisure to undertake a formal appraisal of his subordinate staff. A busy first order manager would not have the time to contemplate such an operation. He would note, of course, who was doing well and who was doing badly, but his assessments would be instinctive and empirical. It would never occur to him that he should devote himself to an abstract appraisal of his staff. If he had an empirical orientation, the whole idea of taking a human resource audit would appear to him as some kind of sour joke. The Leeds factory manager was not an expert in the mystique of questionnaire and form design. What could be more natural than his suggestion that the personnel department should undertake this activity on his behalf? The use of second order administrators of this kind would, in any case, help to give such an exercise a scientific, if somewhat clinical, gloss.

Second order administration is also much encouraged by the prestige which is currently attached to experts of almost all kinds. Psychologists, for example, are supposed to know more about people than the rest of humanity. Why not therefore engage these 'people experts' and set them to work within personnel departments? The growth of second order administration is fuelled by universities and other educational institutions. In general, second order personnel are paid more than those in the first order and consequently have higher status. This, too, greatly encourages the growth of second order professions.

The work undertaken by second order specialists is not essential and therefore the performance of primary tasks does not depend on it. For example, it was evident at Tufted that carpet would continue to be made and sold even if weekly profit flashes and monthly statements were discontinued. There was no tangible connection between the work of the management accounting section and primary tasks. In fact, Tufted had in previous years operated without even semblance of management accounting. The management accounting system at Tufted perfectly illustrated the non-essential character of second order administration.

Tufted provided many examples of how second order administration can impede first order operations. Before the introduction of a marketing department at Tufted the invoicing of customers was quite simple. Invoices carried only information relevant to transactions. This did not meet the requirements of the marketing department which tried to justify its existence by compiling and presenting information on the pattern of company trading. The essential information given on invoices was not of a kind which was readily reducible to generalizations. Consequently, new invoices were introduced which had provision for the inclusion of substantial amounts of coded information. This coded information was not relevant to transactions. For instance, it was not sufficient to give the name of the carpet concerned; the product group to which it belonged also had to be specified. Did the carpet fall within the light domestic category? Or was it a medium duty carpet? The coded product group information would, after processing, enable the marketing department to state what percentage of the company's sales consisted in heavy duty carpet or some other category. A further set of coded information referred to sales areas and to the kind of outlet in which transactions occurred. From information of this sort it was theoretically possible to construct a generalized and quantified description of the company's trading operations. It seemed much better to base policy discussions on information of this sort than to rely solely on guesswork, experience, and common sense.

The point immediately at issue here is not whether this development could be useful in terms of policy; it is rather whether the extra work which it generated served to impede or improve first order operations. The simple task of invoicing had been transformed into a very complicated one. It had as a result become much more time consuming and costly. The process of invoicing now took longer so that transactions were performed less expeditiously. The extra work tended to demoralize those who had to perform it, especially because its relevance was not obvious to them. The volume of coded information became so great that the task of collating it manually proved too daunting to contemplate. This provided a stimulus for Tufted to acquire a computer and a team of data processing experts. This further development caused the costs of the whole exercise to reach altogether disproportionate levels. There could be no doubt about the fact that this served to impede the efficient performance of the primary task. Nor was this offset by a more sensible sales policy. Something useful might be gleaned from the new data collected, but it was obvious that this should be checked against experience and common sense. This was not done at Tufted. It is characteristic of second order specialists to believe that their information somehow displaces that derived directly from first order activity. The damage would be less if second order information was thought to supplement rather than invalidate that of the first order.

The major activity of the management services department consisted in the introduction and maintenance of very complicated payment systems. The industrial engineers in this department took considerable pride in their work. They were very conscious of their own formal qualifications and of their membership of professional institutes. They had acquired the techniques of their profession at the cost of much time and personal effort. Much of their self-esteem was based on their belief that they were professionals doing a professional job. They sincerely believed that they were applying well attested techniques and concepts to the problems of industrial relations at Tufted. The pride and training of these industrial engineers made them insufficiently sensitive to the particular needs of shop floor workers at Tufted. They applied their well attested techniques almost automatically and without proper regard to circumstances. The ineffectiveness of much second order activity is to a large extent attributable to the blinkered attitudes and perceptions of the specialists who undertake it. They tend to operate in self-contained and self-validating worlds.

Shortly before Gray arrived at Tufted the management services department had introduced a number of incentive schemes in various sections on the shop floor. These had had the easily predictable, although unforeseen, result of altering well established differentials. This intensified conflict on the shop floor with the consequence that production itself was adversely affected. The department was, when Gray arrived, preparing a very complex measured day work scheme in an attempt to assuage the discontent in the backing plant. The men in this plant had seen their differential over less skilled operators almost disappear. The scheme being prepared by management services was intensely disliked by the men and these feelings were shared by their supervisors. It was obvious that the men wanted a simple flat rate pay system. Gray saw this, and he at once became an advocate of this demand.

Measured day work is a work-studied system of payment which lacks an explicit incentive element. The simpler pay system demanded by the men could be implemented without the aid of specialists in industrial engineering or work study. An acceptance of a simple pay system would be a blow to the pride of those in management services and a threat to the rationale of their department. The entrenched political interests of specialist departments devoted to second order administration often offer strong resistance to the application of obvious and common sense solutions to problems in first order operations. It was significant that the men in the backing plant did not get their way until after the elimination of the management services department.

The industrial engineers had inflexibly applied preconceptions to a situation in which they were inappropriate. Much the same could be said of the consultants who were responsible for the system of management accounting at Tufted. They described this system as tailor-made to fit the requirements of this company, even though it was perfectly standard. It was hardly surprising that a standard system would fail to accommodate itself to some peculiar, but important, features of the operations at Tufted. For instance, it failed, as has been mentioned, to pay anything like enough regard to the importance of material which represented about 70 per cent of the total cost of production. Instead, it emphasized the importance of machine utilization. The system encouraged the belief that it was sensible to run machines more intensively even if this meant wasting more material. It has also been pointed out that the system encouraged an even greater absurdity: it provided a rationale which indicated that Tufted should produce carpet for which their machinery was generally not well adapted. Again, the value-added doctrine which the system embodied persuaded management at Tufted that it was profitable to produce carpet which could not be readily sold.

The co-ordination of production and sales was poor at Tufted mainly because of the disruptive influence exerted by the accounting system. Such influence as was exerted by the marketing department was also in the same direction. Second order administration can, and often does, seriously impair the co-ordination of first order operations.

Second order administration often provides top management with data that are unrepresentative of first order operations. At Tufted, for example, the management accounts embodied data which seriously misrepresented physical stocks. Muldoon blamed operators for this, because of their failure to follow paperwork routines properly. The import of his argument was always that the system itself was sound. Failings could be attributed to the fact that mistakes were made in its application, and these could be corrected if more resources were made available. Although some of the data might be inaccurate, Muldoon would insist that they were reliable enough to form the basis of serious discussions in the boardroom. He genuinely believed in the validity of the system so that any disparity between it and first order operations meant that the latter and not the former needed changing. His world, like that of the industrial engineers, was self-contained and insulated from empirically based criticism.

Second order administration can have relatively benign, or more strictly speaking neutral, effects on first order operations. For example, the management services department at Tufted regularly prepared data and reports on unit labour costs within the company. It was impossible to attach any tangible empirical meaning to the term 'unit' and as a result this work did not have any significance to line managers. Fortunately, it was destined only for filing within the department which produced it. Had it been that line managers and others were obliged to discuss this work at meetings it would have served to divert their energies from more relevant tasks. In that case the work would have exerted a harmful rather than a neutral influence.

Third order administration
The failure of second order administration to achieve its purpose stimulates the growth of a third order. The failure of the second order is manifested by the fact that the problems which it sets out to solve or alleviate so often remain or become more severe. Second order

activity also creates new problems which demand attention. It has been shown at Tufted, for example, that it produced damaging conflict between staff departments and line management.

Second order administrators distrust the empirical orientation of first order men, and they tend to depict their organizations in abstract terms. The third order administrator accepts the general legitimacy of the process of abstraction even though he might be critical of particular instances of it. The third order administrator constructs his abstractions out of those produced by the second order.

At Tufted there was little in the way of third order administration. Palmer attempted to operate at the third level. He had been instrumental in introducing a complex system of invoicing which he had seen operating elsewhere within the group. This director attempted to extract policy guides from the data derived from invoices. He also tried to relate the information produced by the management accounting system to the activities of the marketing department. Muldoon cast himself very self-consciously in the role of a third order administrator. He attempted to construct far-reaching theories from the data embodied in weekly profit flashes and monthly statements. He also devoted much energy to the task of extending the scope of the system of management accounting, and he tried to refine it and make certain adjustments in its design. Activity of this sort, and that involved in the selection of second order procedures and techniques, is part of the work of the third order administrator. An administrator of this order is concerned with the management of non-essential forms of administration.

Markland had acquired in his previous jobs an addiction for third order administration. He was appalled by the lack of it at Tufted. His addiction partly accounted for the early commitments which he formed in respect of Palmer and Muldoon. The appointment by Markland of two product managers, the two business planning and operations executives, and the industrial relations consultant constituted an attempt to extend the scope of third order administration within Tufted.

Third order administration within the Total Group was concentrated in company headquarters. Here, for example, a team of operations research experts set to work on the company's transport problems. They were displeased by the fact that lorries in the subsidiaries were not used to anything like their full capacity. At Tufted, for example, lorries left more or less full of carpet but returned empty. A planning section was set up at head office to devise ways and schedules to ensure that lorries could pick up loads on their return trips. This, of course, necessitated that time consuming reporting systems were instituted at subsidiaries so that head office could be kept in touch with traffic movements and future transport requirements. The calculations and organization which this operation involved assumed mind-bending proportions and necessitated an increase in the number of planners employed.

The whole idea of a group transport policy was based upon an abstract idea which had been implanted by education in the minds of the operations research specialists. It certainly was not derived from an empirical study of the requirements of subsidiaries.

The Leeds factory was selected by these third order administrators as the distribution centre for the West Riding and Humber regions. The dispatch area of this factory was designed exclusively to handle carpet rolls. It had no facility to handle goods of other kinds. Within a week or so of the introduction of the group transport scheme the whole area became choked with refrigerators, curtains, tins of paint, furniture, and other items. Loaders refused to handle these goods for want of suitable lifting gear. They were driven to protest through strike action. At one time it actually became physically impossible to get carpet out of the factory. Impatient customers complained of delays in delivery. Meanwhile lorries stood outside the loading bay waiting for a signal from head office that a return load was awaiting collection. In the carpet trade prompt delivery can be at least as important as price to customers. The effects of the sophisticated group transport policy on Tufted were obviously very detrimental. In fact, the company lost one of its most important customers as a result of the delays in delivery.

The scheme was naturally resented by resident directors, and privately they were very outspoken in their criticism of it. One day Gray met the director of group transport over lunch in the boardroom at Tufted, and he took the opportunity to launch a devastating attack on the new scheme. This director was at first speechless. Subsequently, as his anger mounted he was driven to rebut the argument of his assailant by saying:

'You don't fucking know what you're fucking talking about.'

After this director had left the room Lennon comforted Gray by saying:

'We know he's as thick as two planks, but we can't do anything about it.'

When Gray suggested that Lennon and the others could have supported the protest, Lennon said simply:

'He outranks us.'

This example typifies the kind of failure which results from committed third order administration.

The difference between the third and second orders is one of degree rather than kind. The second order administrator tends to apply existing routines and systems. The selection of systems, their design and subsequent refinement, is more characteristic of the third order. Again, as we have indicated, the real distinguishing mark of the third order man is that he uses second order data as the basis for his theorizing. The really accomplished third order man uses data from several second order sources simultaneously. In business schools this is referred to as 'cross-fertilization' or described as a 'multi-disciplinary'. The totality of management is thought to consist of a series of second order disciplines united symphonically in the third order; it is not thought to be understood through empirically based studies of organizations.

Job specifications: a feature of the second and third orders

Johnson's and Leyland's work on job specification provided a good illustration of the characteristics of second and third order work. As we have seen, job specifications are not required in a purely first order organization provided that overstaffing does not occur. In such an organization the work of everyone is both essential and inter-dependent. The failure of anyone to perform his work has adverse effects on that of others and on the accomplishment of the primary task. In these circumstances a person who fails to perform his work adequately will find himself under pressure from others either to improve his performance or leave. As long as overstaffing is avoided everyone will have at least enough to do and they will therefore welcome the help of others.

Overstaffing creates a shortage of work, and people tend to respond to this by jealously guarding work and by creating it artificially. Job specifications have their origins in circumstances of this kind. The growth of second and third order administration intensifies the need for job specifications. Second and third order administration is not operationally dependent on first order activity. Indeed, much of this book is an illustration of how these higher orders actually serve to impede the accomplishment of primary tasks.

Departments devoted to second order activities try so far as is possible to be independent of each other. For instance, at Tufted the accounting department relied to some extent on cost data prepared by management services. It was hoped that the installation of the new computer would enable the accounting department to extricate itself from its dependence on management services. The latter department did not resent this because its members would continue to produce the data concerned, for internal use. Second order activities are therefore not only independent of the first order, they also tend to be independent of each other.

The work of second order departments is both non-essential and non-interdependent. The failure of second order specialists to perform their jobs has not therefore the consequences which are associated with shortcomings among first order personnel. At Tufted, carpet would continue to be made and sold even if the management accountants and those employed in the marketing department did not do any work. Job specifications provide a means whereby one can discipline second order personnel when they fail to perform their jobs. Job specifications will list the duties and, possibly, the performance standards which such employees are expected to fulfil. Failure to comply with these standards can be used to justify disciplinary action or even dismissal. Again, success in meeting or exceeding the standards specified in job descriptions might be thought to merit extra rewards or promotion.

Third order personnel are only dependent on those in the second order in the rather artificial sense that their existence arises out of the inevitable operational failure of that previous order. Job specifications tend to become more recondite as one moves towards the third order. This is inescapable because the third order operate at a higher level of abstraction.

The behaviour of first order personnel is to a great extent structured by operational necessity and by the fact of inter-dependence. Job specifications attempt to regulate the behaviour of those who are not bound by such constraints.

Problems associated with job specifications would not have arisen at Tufted in the absence of both overstaffing, and departments devoted to second and third order activity. In these circumstances the production director would administer the factories; the purchasing director would buy; and the sales director would sell. Of course, it would be possible to describe these and other jobs in much greater detail, but the resulting statements would be descriptive of what people actually did; they could not be used to evaluate or co-ordinate.

Confusion and the need for co-ordination arises out of overstaffing and the growth of self-contained administrative departments. At Tufted an important customer wanted the company to develop a new design for their exclusive use—who should negotiate with him? Sales or marketing, or design? A high proportion of the yarn breakages occurred on a particular machine—who should negotiate with the machine supplier? Purchasing or production? Job specifications attempt to predict such clashes and to solve the resulting problems by predetermining responsibilities.

Fourth order administration

The third order must serve to compound the failures of the second order; it could not possibly be otherwise. The idea that there might be a fourth order of administration which attempts to correct their combined failure by creating abstractions out of those employed in the third order which were, in turn, derived from those of the second seems highly improbable. The human mind was not designed by its Maker to operate at a third level of abstraction.

Someone must head a hierarchical organization. In fact his first, and perhaps, only duty may be to occupy that position and behave with a dignity appropriate to that station. In the larger corporations he is surrounded by supporting dignitaries. The chairman of Total Furnishings played this role of a dignitary; his life style and his self-importance testified to that fact.

Idleness, although not necessarily leisure, characterizes life in the fourth order of administration. Companies are work institutions, and idleness is the sweetest reward that they can offer. It has a certain illicit fascination; it represents a triumph over the dominant and pro-claimed values of a work organization. It exists at all levels. On the shop floor operators speak of 'good skives', 'easy numbers', and 'soft corners'. These are highly valued. In the higher echelons of business idleness is seldom acknowledged by explicit expressions of this kind, but it is nevertheless assiduously cultivated. At these levels it reaches the sophistication of an art form. The social and operational isolation inescapable in these higher reaches brings with it compensations, and it actively encourages aristocratic attitudes. An individual can obtain arrogant pleasure from arbitrating upon issues about which he has little, if any, understanding.

The fourth order was surprisingly well developed within Tufted itself. The idleness which pervaded the boardroom has been com-mented upon already. The resident directors had surprisingly little work to do. They had, through appointments and delegation, relieved themselves of one task after another. Smith took delegation to extremes. His appointment of a general sales manager meant that he entirely relieved himself of day-to-day duties. Gray noticed that it was necessary to engage resident directors in hours of chit-chat before there was any chance that they might get down to business. He found that the urgent tasks which he sometimes entrusted to them were left unattended in his absence. This he realized was due to laziness rather than obstructiveness. Markland, who was in fact hard working, was intensely irritated by the indolence of the board. The resident direc-tors even used their conspicuous idleness to taunt and mock his efforts.

Outright idleness is less pervasive among second and third order administrators. Here laziness is mainly exemplified through an obsessive attachment to routines. Gray, for instance, could not for a long time even find out what each category of labour at Tufted actually earned. How could he possibly fulfil his assigned task of adviser in industrial relations in the absence of such elementary first order information? The resistance of specialist departments to his requests was due to the fact that existing administrative routines did not provide the information which he sought. When the management services department was pressurized by Markland into providing this information it showed itself incapable of exercising the necessary common sense. People hide behind routines, painfully acquired techniques, and professional vocabularies in order to avoid the necessity for thought. After years of such avoidance they render themselves incapable of work.

Typical business organizations have retinues of auxiliaries which enable executives to adopt the life style appropriate to the fourth order. These auxiliaries perform roles analogous to those of servants in grand households. Tufted was much less favoured in this respect than was the head office at Total. Even so it was not entirely lacking in these provisions. Markland, for instance, had his own personal secretary, but a certain note of austerity was struck by the fact that none of the other directors were granted this privilege. In many, if not most, companies there is a gross under-utilization of secretaries because they are allocated on the basis of status rather than work requirements. A secretary is there to answer the executive's telephone in his absence, to exclude unwelcome visitors, to relieve him of the necessity to deal with most of his correspondence, to book theatre tickets and tables in restaurants, and so on. She relieves him of irksome tasks so that he is free to devote time and energy to the important work, such as that involved in policy formation.

The privacy of the boardroom at Tufted was maintained by a rota of receptionists who performed duties not altogether different to that of butlers in aristocratic establishments. Again, the company employed people who acted as chauffeurs to executives so that in moments of stress they might be relieved of driving.

The company's dining facilities, even in the boardroom itself, were rather utilitarian. Tufted was not renowned for the quality of its cuisine. However, frequent sponsored visits to restaurants and hotels helped to mitigate the hardship which this implied.

Even if the surroundings at Tufted were much less opulent than those at company headquarters there were some privileges which its executives enjoyed which were not readily available in the purely

110

administrative branches. At Tufted there were requisitionable resources in the form of motor mechanics, plumbers, carpenters, carpet fitters, and the like. In some ways Tufted resembled a landed estate; it too had a useful selection of tradesmen.

Occasionally, the fourth order at Tufted indulged itself in a slight and harmless extension of the idea of 'the working lunch'—'the round of golf with business associates'. Gammage and Birtwhistle were especially partial to this diversion.

12
Executive brainstorming

The strategy

During his time at business school, Markland had learned the techniques of brainstorming. This activity was said to release the best ideas from a group of people. He devised the agenda for the Middlesbrough meeting with this aim in mind. The operating board was to be split into syndicates to examine, in detail, individual aspects of the company's business and then a full session of the board would be convened, during which, a spokesman for each syndicate would report back. Such a structure would, in Markland's view, tap the energies and knowledge of all the participants and this would clarify all of the issues.

At varying times during the Friday afternoon, members of the operating board set out for the motel in Middlesbrough. The route was very easy, being confined mainly to dual carriageways or motorways, but it was extremely tedious. The fuel saving fifty mile per hour limit was being rigorously obeyed, and any malefactor who dared exceed the speed incurred the wrath of fellow motorists in a fury of flashing lights. The gloom of this journey, engendered by the snail's pace and by the forbidding greyness of a cold winter's afternoon was scarcely dispelled by the functional austerity of the chosen motel.

Spirits were somewhat revived by a few drinks in the bar and by an expensive, if somewhat tasteless, meal in the restaurant. After dinner the directors armed themselves with drinks and dutifully followed Markland into the conference room.

Each participant had been supplied with an agenda, broken down into three sessions. The sessions were identical in pattern, being divided into syndicate discussions followed by meetings of the entire group. The first group meeting was to take place on Saturday morning, and the syndicate was to be convened immediately following Markland's opening remarks. The agenda for the first session was:

112

CONDITIONS UNDER WHICH WE
WILL BE TRADING
Subject:
(a) The economy
Chairman—Markland
Group members—Birtwhistle, Muldoon
(b) Supplies
Chairman—Tenniswood
Group members—Leyland, Smith,
Gammage
(c) Home and export markets
Chairman—Palmer
Group members—Johnson, Lennon

Markland had clearly put a great deal of thought into this agenda, and he had consciously put Leyland and Johnson in separate groups. These executives would, no doubt, ensure that the requisite amount of cerebral activity would take place.

His opening remarks, to the assembly, were designed to ensure that the right attitudes would be engendered. He rose to his feet and said:

'Gentlemen, I've decided to hold this conference away from the factory because I want us to be entirely free from interruptions. We've got some very important decisions to make this weekend. We've got to decide where we are trying to go and how we are going to get there. We're here to decide our objectives, our priorities, and our overall strategy. This is a make or break year for Tufted. I'm determined to make it a make year. I'm sure that everyone here has something vital to contribute both to formulating our strategy and to the task of seeing it through. As you see, I've divided you into study groups so that we can look at our key operating areas systematically and in sequence. I suggest that we take a quick drink or two in the bar and assemble in syndicates in half an hour.'

After this peroration the group dutifully filled their glasses and then repaired, in syndicates, to discuss their appointed topics.

Saturday morning

Gray arrived just in time for coffee. He had missed Markland's report on the economy. Markland's thinking on this subject was influenced by a highly optimistic report on the carpet industry which had just been produced by a government sponsored agency. This report described Britain as the 'Detroit of the European carpet industry'. The managing director had listed a number of factors which, he asserted, gave the industry as a whole a substantial competitive edge over continental manufacturers. The costs of material were much lower in the

United Kingdom. This was also true, he asserted, of labour cost. The depreciation of the pound in relation to several continental currencies, he contended, served to increase still further this competitive advantage. In comparison with Britain continental countries were, he pointed out, relatively 'undercarpeted'. This, he argued, provided Tufted with tremendous opportunities abroad. The Three Day Week was, he maintained, only a temporary setback. Demand at home had so far kept up very well and there was every reason to believe that things would soon return to normal. He concluded:

'If, we get our product mix and our price structure right I'm sure we can face the future on the domestic market with confidence.'

Tenniswood presented his report on supplies immediately after coffee. He concentrated on the availability and price of synthetic fibres. The supply of many fibres was, he argued, likely to be threatened by the pollution problems facing Japanese producers. This was forcing them to construct plants outside Japan with the result that an important source of fibre was, to some extent, being undermined. He continued by expressing the belief that the prices of man-made fibres would continue to increase in line with general inflation. The main problem on the supply side was, he maintained, availability rather than price.

Suddenly, Markland shouted at a couple of hotel staff who were tidying up a bar on the far side of the room:

'Don't you realize this is a confidential meeting. Get out. This is intolerable. I shall complain to the hotel manager.'

Meekly, the hotel staff complied.

After this diversion Tenniswood continued with his presentation in the same dull monotone which had characterized it so far. He argued that although wool prices were high they were, nevertheless, much more stable than those of man-made fibres. He continued by expressing the opinion that the price of many of these would soon overtake that of wool. This opinion, he sought to support, by means of an elaborate analysis of trends in sheep farming, both at home and abroad. He concluded by saying that it would be good sense to use much more of this traditional material in the future.

Markland glanced at his watch and said:

'We'll take a break now. I'm sure we could all do with a drink. Brian will give his report after lunch.'

On the way to the bar Markland remarked to Gray:

'Tenniswood was very good, don't you think?'

He received the following uncompromising rejoinder:

'What an idiot. He can't even order what is wanted for tomorrow's production. He would be doing us a favour if he went to live on a sheep farm.'

Saturday afternoon

The television in the bar was tuned to ITV, which was showing *On the Ball*. A number of directors would have preferred to be taking their usual places in the stand at Elland Road, and a few of them allowed their eyes to stray to the set. Markland was holding court in the bar, and he was displeased by this competitive attraction. As the bar was quite full, he sensed that the management would not accede to a request to turn the set off.

'We can't talk business over this drivel, let's go into lunch.'

As soon as he had finished eating, Markland stood up and said:

'As we're running behind schedule, we'll start straight away. We'll take coffee in the meeting.'

Palmer's presentation was extremely dull and after half an hour Markland cut him short and instructed everyone to continue syndicate work with the following agenda:

▶ SESSION 2   STRENGTHS AND WEAKNESSES OF THE COMPANY
         (a) Production facilities and know-how
            Chairman—Lennon
            Group members—Tenniswood, Johnson, Gray
         (b) Customers—home and export
            Chairman—Smith
            Group members—Birtwhistle, Leyland
         (c) Cost structure and controls
            Chairman—Muldoon
            Group members—Markland, Palmer, Gammage

Gray joined the syndicate headed by Lennon. The latter stated a few obvious things about the factories, and as all those present seemed in agreement Gray suggested that it would be a good idea if they went to the bar to await the outcome of the other group meetings. Johnson and Lennon accepted this invitation with alacrity, but Tenniswood pleaded that he had some urgent work to attend to.

Lennon was the first to report when the general meeting was reconvened. His presentation was exceedingly brief in comparison with those of Markland and Tenniswood. He spoke in simple terms about the main problems involved in running the factories. He talked about the 'buggeration factor' caused by short production runs and frequent design changes. He concluded:

'The machines are designed to produce carpet in bulk. My life would be made easier if I only had to make single loop unbacked

115

white carpet. Frequent product changes and short runs cause an enormous wastage of material and a lot of downtime.'

Lennon then called on Gray to make some comments on industrial relations. Gray stated that the wage system at Tufted had become much too complicated. It should, he contended, be simplified. He also pointed out that the operators at Cleckheaton were on different rates of pay to those at Leeds, even though they did the same jobs and worked on the same kind of machines. This was, he asserted, beginning to cause trouble which could become very serious in the near future. It was essential, he argued, to make a big effort to correct anomalies of this kind. He concluded by expressing the view that progress on these matters was possible in spite of the restrictions imposed by statutory incomes policy.

This combined presentation scarcely took half an hour and failed to promote any discussion.

Smith's presentation was even briefer than that of Lennon. He expressed the view that the home market was more profitable to the company than the export trade. He pointed out that the activities of salesmen at home were under his direct control. The company had, he argued, little control over operations on the continent.

Markland strongly dissociated himself from the latter opinion, but agreed with Smith that it would be unwise to concentrate on exports to an extent which would undermine Tufted's share of the home market.

The mood of the meeting was gradually becoming euphoric. Both Markland and Tenniswood started to talk expansively about future profits. Palmer joined in and attempted to outdo the other speakers in his predictions about prospects for the future. After a while Gray found talk of this kind more than he could stand. He could see, through a window, the motorway in the distance. On it, vehicles crawled like snails in the gathering dusk. The whole nation seemed to him to be operating at half-pace. Quite suddenly he shouted out:

'You're all fools to believe that you're going to make a huge profit. We're at the start of the most serious recession since the end of the war. We should be talking about how we are going to stay in business, not about how much money we are going to make. The arguments which you've all been putting forward ignore obvious things like the collapse in the building industry. Surely, our home sales are related to the number of new houses completed?'

After some awkward moments the discussion continued as though this intervention had not occurred, although for the moment the general mood became more restrained.

After a short break for afternoon tea Muldoon indicated his readiness to report on behalf of his study group. Leyland and Gray exchanged surprised glances as Muldoon proclaimed the virtues of the new computer. They were under the impression that Markland had committed himself to its cancellation and had communicated this to Muldoon. Leyland made one or two points about what he considered were inadequacies in the data collection system, but these were loudly and emphatically brushed aside by Muldoon.

As soon as he had finished Gray launched into a bitter attack on the premises underlying the accounting system. Muldoon countered this attack by claiming that there was nothing inherently wrong with the system. The failure lay, he asserted, in the fact that insufficient resources were at present being devoted to its development. The effectiveness of the system would be much enhanced, he contended, by the acquisition of the new computer and by the recruitment of expert staff. Gray retorted that this remedy served to compound the waste and futility embodied in the system. This theme was taken up by Johnson, but Muldoon steadfastly continued to maintain that there was nothing wrong with the system.

Suddenly, Gray changed the direction of his attack and asked Gammage:

'When did you last look at the management accounts?'

Gammage confessed that he never looked at them and was quite unable to understand them. One by one Gray asked the other resident directors the same question. All of them, with one minor exception, had to admit that they did not personally consult the accounts. They were forced into these submissions as they knew that otherwise Gray would have asked them to explain the meaning of a set of accounts. Lennon was the last to face the inquisitor. He admitted that he found the monthly statements were beyond his understanding, but he feebly added that he found the weekly profit flashes useful.

This proved too much for Markland who shouted:

'What do you do that you would not have done because of the weekly flashes?'

Lennon blurted out:

'I just think it's nice to know whether one is doing badly or well.'

Markland replied:

'What's the use of a system which tells you that you are doing badly if it does not suggest what you ought to do about it?'

Markland concluded this section of the meeting by indicating that he had changed his mind about the value of the management accounting system.

'It led,' he said, 'to the absurd situation where people actually seemed to believe that it was profitable to make carpet which could not be sold.'

He concluded by expressing the opinion that it would be better if the accounting department restricted itself to bookkeeping and other essential operations.

Markland symbolized a new order by requiring Johnson and Gray to sit either side of him at dinner. At Markland's insistence Gray placed an order for a dozen bottles of wine and several decanters of port. During the meal Muldoon continued to talk about the new computer. Suddenly, that chatter stopped when Markland said:

'You're not having your bloody computer!'

Muldoon would not believe his ears, and he protested that as the contract was signed there would be substantial cancellation charges. He received a reply which could not be misunderstood.

'I don't care what it costs, you're not going to have a new computer.'

Muldoon's self-confidence and self-assurance instantly crumpled, and he became as white as a sheet. He asked to be excused and disappeared for about two hours. When he returned to the assembled company, which by now had transferred itself to the bar, he had regained his former bounce and confidence. Gray, especially, was puzzled as to the cause of this remarkably rapid recovery.

Sunday

Markland had arranged with the hotel manager to provide an early breakfast so that the meeting could re-start at eight o'clock. The only absentee at breakfast was Markland himself. No one knew his whereabouts, but he appeared as if from nowhere a minute or so before the meeting was due to start. The agenda was:

► SESSION 3   STRATEGY 1974/1975
                   (a) Product strategy
                        Chairman—Palmer
                        Group members—Smith, Gray,
                        Leyland, Lennon
                   (b) Market strategy
                        Chairman—Palmer
                        Group members—Markland,
                        Tenniswood, Johnson, Gammage,
                        Muldoon

Except for the first half hour which was spent in syndicates the entire morning was taken up by Birtwhistle who had brought a whole car load of carpet samples. He explained at great length the technical properties of each type of carpet. Gray was bored to distraction by the protracted tedium of it all, and he was surprised by the interest

and attention which Markland showed throughout the whole morning. When they were going into lunch Markland said to him:
'That was absolutely first-class.'
Gray felt exhausted; he took the line of least resistance and agreed.
After lunch Palmer made the assertion that 60 per cent of the sales effort went into about 5 per cent of sales. It would, he argued, be a good idea to close down the cutting room and eliminate the cut lengths service. He asserted that perfectly good rolls were often cut into shorter lengths to satisfy the whims of unimportant customers. The cut lengths business could, he contended, be transferred to another subsidiary within the Total group. This suggestion came as something of a bombshell; it had not been put forward in the preparatory discussion which had taken place within the market strategy syndicate.

Before anyone had a chance to question Palmer about how he had arrived at his figures or whether it was true that most of the misdirected sales effort actually occurred in relation to the cut lengths service the suggestion was seized upon by Markland. The latter deployed the full force of his rhetoric and authority in support of Palmer's proposal. A mood of optimism quickly established itself within the meeting as a whole. Only Smith expressed reservations about the proposal. He pointed out that other manufacturers were either introducing or expanding their cut lengths service. He admitted, under cross questioning from Markland, that his opposition to the proposal was guided by instinct rather than logic. Eventually, he indicated that if the cutting room was to be closed then, this was the time to do it. Johnson and Leyland were fully won over by Markland's eloquence. Gray said nothing because he could not think of any counter arguments. However, he had a respect for Smith's experience of the carpet trade and he wondered to himself if something obvious was being overlooked.

The closure of the cutting room would involve the elimination of about seventy jobs on the shop floor. Markland indicated that this presented an opportunity to reorganize the management structure.

At the end of the meeting Markland was clearly elated and he took Gray aside to tell him how wonderfully simple it all was. The latter replied that things might not seem so simple in the cold light of dawn. His last words to Markland before he left to collect his baggage were:
'I don't know how you can stand Palmer.'

The 50 mph limit gave Gray ample leisure for reflection on the way home. He was confused, and no longer felt confident in his own judgement. He began to doubt the wisdom of earlier advice concerning the replacement of the board members and wondered whether Markland had not, after all, showed a certain maturity in not yielding to the temptation to use the axe. He even thought to himself that

Markland might after all mobilize the resident directors into an effective group. However, in the following weeks he began to dismiss these thoughts as weakness on his part.

Markland's summary
On Monday, Markland dictated the following memorandum for circulation among the members of the Operating Board.

► PRIMARY BUSINESS OBJECTIVES

	Last half		
	1973/74	*1974/75*	*1975/76*
Sales	£10 000 000	£20 000 000	£25 000 000
Square yards	8 770 000	17 391 300	20 000 000
Gross profit	1 300 000	3 000 000	4 000 000
Net profit	700 000	1 750 000	3 000 000

TUFTED CARPETS LTD, BUSINESS MISSION
When Ford decided to make his Model T, he made a fundamental marketing decision, and a statement of business mission that concentrated his entire organization on the company's goal.

He looked at the amount of disposable income people could probably afford to spend on a motor car—and set out to capture that latent demand with a product that would give him a satisfactory profit.

The product was the Model T, priced where he felt the major percentage of that latent market was—and the process he selected for production was mass volume production.

A complex product like this required long runs of the same unit to satisfy the market demand—and make a profit.

So with the carpet market. For centuries carpets have been the proud possession of affluent sectors of societies. The Tufted manufacturing process took advantage of the mass markets latent desire for carpet floor coverings, but at a price they could afford.

This process enabled mass production methods to be applied to a traditional art. Inevitably compromises had to be made. Limitation on the number of colourways in design, length of production runs and quality of the end product.

The tufting process has overcome many of these problems in its techniques and quantity of output. It has not however significantly altered the core of its purpose for being—to satisfy the mass markets demand for a product at a price that gives value to the consumer and profit to the producer.

Products that can't be 'mass produced'—and by definition have mass markets—can't possibly conform with the business mission of a tufter, nor can they make a profit. They may satisfy customers, designers, and marketing executives; but they can never satisfy shareholders.

Imagine Henry Ford trying to introduce a few hundred Lagondas and Mazeratis into his mass production process.

Valuable resources oriented towards the Model T would be sucked away in disproportionate quantities. The conveyor belts would have to be altered because of the different dimensions; special painters and finishers would have to be recruited to handle this sophisticated up-market product; the old sales force might have a few contacts or outlets that could take these products, but the vast mass would be of no use to this project; stocks of raw materials and end products would build up—and get damaged and repaired in the warehouse.

However, Henry's management accounts, based on allocating overheads on a 'units of output' basis would record a very lucrative gross profit—right up to the closing down sale.

The situation at Tufted Carpets Ltd is not dissimilar to the Henry Ford analogy. Our plant has been designed as a mass production unit, and if we are to make the best of it, we must use it to serve the mass market we are after.

We may have tried to invent complex systems to account for the additional cost of making more sophisticated products, but this is only dodging the issue. Unless the product is mass producible and mass marketable it is not for Tufted Carpets Ltd.

BUSINESS MISSION STATEMENT

Tufted Carpets Ltd is in the business of satisfying the mass markets demand for carpet floorcoverings, with products that are suitable for mass production techniques—at the level of profit defined in its financial objectives.

Every product market (new or old), customer, group, and business system must be tested against this statement of our business mission to see if it fits—if it doesn't fit—don't do it.

13
Mass execution

Confirmation of a decision

Overstaffing had not been discussed at the meeting in Middlesbrough, but it was evident that some redundancies would occur if the decision to close the cutting room was implemented. On his return to Tufted, Markland set the head of management services to work on a quantitative assessment of the cut lengths service. This assessment confirmed that most of the bad debts and slow payers were concentrated in this section of the business. It was also shown that about half the invoice work was generated by the cut lengths service even though it only accounted for about ten per cent of sales measured in terms of square yards. Again, it was demonstrated that most of the customer complaints and rejections related to cut lengths. This was not surprising because the company offered a cut lengths service over most of its product range. Often customers had to wait for long periods until a section of a rarely produced carpet became available.

Markland was committed to the closure of the cutting room because he saw that he could use this as an excuse both to remove certain people from the organization and justify other actions. He was pleased to hear from Palmer that the distribution company within Total Furnishings was prepared to take over the cut lengths business. Smith had been sent to see two important customers who took most of their orders in cut lengths to try to persuade them to transfer their business to the distribution company. He received short shrift from both, and one of them was reputed to have thrown Tufted pattern books into a river. Markland regarded this setback as a small price to pay for the closure of the cutting room. Meanwhile, he had approached the chairman and obtained permission to go ahead with the closure.

At Middlesbrough Smith had pointed out that some other companies seemed to run successful cut lengths services and he indicated that he did not know why Tufted was unable to emulate them. In fact, such a service could only be operated efficiently at Tufted if customer choice were restricted to best selling lines. It was incredible that something so obvious should be overlooked. The retention of the cutting room was, for this reason, entirely consistent with the new product strategy. In the context of the company as a whole it was absurd to argue that the cutting room was the cause of an excessive amount of paper work.

Markland declares a redundancy

In the week following the Middlesbrough meeting Markland called Gray into his office and told him that the closure of the cutting room had been confirmed by the chairman. He also suggested that this provided an opportunity to make reductions elsewhere in the organization. He mentioned, in particular, his desire to get rid of the factory manager, the head of management services, and the personnel manager. Gray agreed that such changes were highly desirable. Markland asked him:

'Do you think I should dismiss them as part of a management re-organization or do you think that they should be made redundant?'

After pondering this question for a few moments Gray replied:

'It would be more honest to get rid of them as part of a re-organization, but you might have to justify why you dismiss some rather than others. They could appeal to a tribunal and claim unfair dismissal. That could be awkward. I think it would be easier to make them redundant although it will cost quite a bit in redundancy payments.'

Markland thought for a while, nodded his agreement and said:

'I think we should be generous. I've in mind one and a half times the statutory minimum. I've had experience of firings before and it's much better to get rid of them on the spot. There's no point in making people work out their notices.'

Gray replied:

'I don't think that's a good idea. A chap who has been here for years will feel insulted and degraded if you just show him the door. What are the unions going to say? They'll want to be consulted in advance. It's possible that they could take industrial action if people are fired on the spot. Relations could be soured for a long time to come.'

Markland protested that he would, after all, be softening the blow by offering generous payments. This did not satisfy Gray who said:

'I would start by offering the minimum you can, then under pressure raise this to the figure you've got in mind. This would enable the trade union officials and shop stewards to emerge from the negotiations with credit.'

Markland had by now become very angry and he shouted:

'You kept on telling me that the books are always wrong and now you're telling me to play it by the letter. I've had experience of this sort of thing. If they have to work out a period of notice, they hang around the place like festering sores. They infect everyone else with their discontent. To do as you suggest would be perfectly nonsensical. They will be given their money and cards and shown the door. That's the only realistic way of dealing with the situation. My mind is made up.'

The next day in the boardroom Markland declared a redundancy. He announced that the decision to close the cutting room had been confirmed and this would involve about a ten per cent reduction in sales. It was, he contended, desirable that a corresponding reduction in staff overheads was achieved. Each director and Muldoon was instructed to draw up lists immediately. The staff in the sales office would, he declared, be reduced by about half and there would have to be some reductions in the number of salesmen. He indicated that fewer of these would now be required as the closure of the cut lengths service meant that visits to small retailers would not have to be made. He suggested that Leyland could help Smith to draw up lists. The main area in which redundancies would occur would obviously be in the cutting room itself, and this came under the jurisdiction of Lennon. The latter was to be assisted by Johnson. Palmer was told to discuss his list with Gray who would be visiting the factory on the following day. The remaining members of the operating board were told to make token reductions in their departments.

The motel meeting

Less than a week after the Middlesbrough meeting the lists of those who were to be made redundant were, Markland was informed, ready. He immediately booked a room at a nearby motel, because he believed that it was necessary to maintain the utmost secrecy over the whole operation. For this reason the redundancy lists were hand written by the directors themselves. He feared that a tea lady, or some other intruder, might overhear a remark as she entered the boardroom. He also feared that some tell-tale scrap of paper might be left either in the boardroom or an office. Again, he believed that it was impossible to conclude the redundancy arrangements with the required secrecy and speed if members of the operating board had to answer telephone calls. For all these reasons it seemed to him essential to hold a meeting off the premises. Of course, the fact that the entire operating board had disappeared on the Friday of the previous week to an unknown destination had not escaped the notice of the staff. The whole factory was rife with rumour and speculation which was still further intensified by this subsequent departure.

The motel room proved to be a bar which at the time was unused.

Johnson noticed that one of its walls was symbolically decorated with a sabre. At first the meeting went smoothly enough. It became clear that the heads of both management services and personnel would be made redundant. Apart from two junior work study assistants all the members of the former department were listed. All the resident directors presented lists which satisfied Markland, but Muldoon remained silent. Gray drew the attention of the meeting to this and asked the commercial manager for his list. Much to Markland's visible annoyance Muldoon replied in evasive and barely coherent terms, and Gray continued his examination in altogether harsher and more direct terms. He said:

'Every member of this board had produced a list except you. They are making sacrifices. What's so special about you or your department which absolves you from the obligation to draw up a list?'

Muldoon protested that his department was grossly overworked and that it was senseless to reduce staff. He added that the cancellation of the new computer and the failure to appoint additional staff meant that he had already made an appreciable sacrifice. The resident directors showed by looks rather than words that they agreed with Gray. Markland had for some time been uncharacteristically silent, but suddenly, he erupted furiously:

'If I don't have a list with ten names on it by Monday,' he almost screamed at Muldoon, 'I will draw up one myself and your name will be at the top.'

Muldoon's wife typed him a list over the weekend. This contained the names of some systems analysts who had been recruited in the expectation of the new computer. One of these had only been with the company for a week. The remaining names were those of very junior staff.

Markland stated emphatically that everyone should be fired on the spot simultaneously. He reiterated the arguments which he had deployed in his conversation with Gray. Palmer enthusiastically supported these and indicated that he had experience which confirmed the sense of what Markland was saying. He expressed his opinion crudely by saying:

'Get them off the plot.'

The meeting agreed that the redundancy would take place in a fortnight's time on a Thursday. This was preferable to a Friday because Markland felt that the staff would expect a redundancy to be declared on a pay day. A Thursday would, he believed, catch them off balance. Smith indicated that he would call the redundant salesmen to London on the appointed day so as to fire them personally. He was most anxious that the timing of these dismissals should coincide exactly with those in the factory itself.

Boardroom events

On the Monday after the motel meeting the mood in the boardroom was one of elation. The atmosphere was pregnant with nervous excitement. Board members attempted to conceal their tension and guilt by a forced jollity. Over morning coffee Markland suddenly announced that he had decided to bring the redundancy forward a week to the coming Thursday. This suggestion was not challenged, perhaps because the directors were already finding the tension of waiting and the strain of secrecy hard to bear.

Muldoon indicated that the new arrangement would leave him very little time to obtain the necessary forms from the Department of Employment and Productivity. With reckless disregard for his own safety and that of others he charged out of the boardroom and the building. After jumping into his car he drove in great haste to the local labour exchange to collect the necessary papers.

When he arrived next morning, Gray found the boardroom full. Everyone was there with the exception of Markland, who had the previous evening gone to London. Lennon broke the news to him. Gray found himself seated at the head of the table with all eyes turned in his direction. The jollity of the boardroom had, for the moment, given way to a very sombre mood. After a pause Lennon continued:

'Speaking for myself I don't see why we can't have a phased redundancy. It's not necessary to fire men there and then.'

Gray was sympathetic to this view, but reminded Lennon of the decision that had been reached at the motel. He continued:

'David is very certain about this in his own mind, but I must confess that bringing the date forward is a bit of a shock to me. It doesn't give any time for second thoughts. If I was given marching orders without notice I would be very hurt. The whole thing is a deep affront to the staff. In my opinion the unions should be consulted. What's going to happen if they should black this place or something?'

Tenniswood spoke in support of this view and maintained that it was bad form not to consult the unions in advance. There seemed to be general agreement in the boardroom in support of this opinion, and Gray said:

'I want to be quite sure that we understand the position. There seems to be general agreement in favour of putting off the redundancy until Thursday week so as to allow time for consultation with the unions. I think we ought to take a vote. Those in favour of this proposal please show.'

Every member of the boardroom raised his hand in support.

A few minutes later Markland entered the boardroom from the adjoining office. Gray stood up and turned around to face him. The rest of the boardroom focused their eyes firmly on the managing director. He looked tense and tight-lipped even before Gray spoke. The latter came straight to the point by saying:

'We've taken a vote and all of us are in favour of putting the redundancy back a week so as to consult the unions.'

This was the first time that the consultant had openly defied the managing director. Markland was obviously livid, but he said quietly:

'I will have to think about it. I'll give you a decision in ten minutes.'

When he returned he looked much more relaxed and said:

'We'll do it your way.'

Within the next hour he had contacted some local union officials and arranged to meet them.

Markland met the local official of the supervisors' union in a pub. He indicated to him that the monthly staff concerned would receive a month's salary in lieu of notice and one and a half times the statutory compensation for redundancy. He agreed to meet this official at the Leeds factory in order to explain further the scope of the redundancy and to provide him with the names of those who were to be laid off. The local representative of the clerks' union was unable to attend this preliminary meeting, but agreed to come to the factory on a later date.

On the next evening Markland met the local official of the manual workers' union whose members were involved in the redundancy. He told Johnson subsequently that this official thanked him 'brokenly' for the generosity of the severance terms.

Both representatives from the staff unions met Markland a day or so later at the Leeds factory. They were informed of the extent of the redundancy and the reasons which had occasioned it, and they were invited to a subsequent meeting at the factory the following Thursday. Markland told them that shop stewards from the factory would also be present.

The tension in the boardroom mounted as the deadline approached. Palmer recounted to Johnson how he had had his tyres slashed and his windscreen broken when he worked at another factory after a redundancy had been declared. This made Johnson more than a shade apprehensive because he felt that he might be perceived by many as the villain of the piece. The guilt which he, and others, experienced became rather oppressive. The day before the redundancy he looked out of a window and saw a man of about sixty struggling to his car over slush and snow which formed ridges on the tarmac. He remembered seeing this man's name on one of the lists. How long had this poor old sod been coming here, he wondered, to himself? Sentimentally, he thought of the open fire and dutiful wife awaiting the return of this breadwinner. He met Markland on his way down the corridor and was greeted with the remark:

'Don't look so fed up, I'll find someone for you to fire.'

The irony of it all was that Johnson had attached the wrong name to the man of unsure gait in the car park. On the following Monday he was surprised to see him once again making his way to the waiting vehicle.

The day of executions

The boardroom had assumed that Markland himself would be firing the monthly staff. On the fateful Thursday he assembled Johnson, Lennon, and Palmer in his office at 9.15 a.m. He stood up and said:

'I want the monthly staff who are not being fired assembled in the boardroom before we start. At 10.00 a.m. I will address them with Johnson while you two do the firing in this office. The cheques and letters are all here and have been checked by Muldoon. Get them in here one by one and be as fast as possible. Find some way of letting me know when you've finished.'

As he went through the door he added the afterthought:

'Make sure they leave the premises.'

Johnson was given the job of ringing up those who were not to be fired. By now, several people in the factory had begun to suspect that something was afoot. Johnson did not know most of those he telephoned. One of these expressed his apprehension to a woman colleague after he had received the request to go straight to the boardroom.

'Who,' he said, 'is this Johnson?'

She replied:

'Oh, he's the hatchet man they've hired.'

She did not know at that stage that her own sense of security was entirely misplaced.

Palmer and Lennon decided to take the twenty or so monthly staff to be made redundant in order of seniority. The first to be called was Cuthbertson, the Leeds factory manager. Only the day before Gray had been mildly surprised by the way in which this manager had been addressed over the telephone by Lennon who had said:

'You're doing a grand job, keep it up.'

Just before he put the receiver down he winked at Gray and added:

'Good lad.'

On Cuthbertson's departure the news spread like wildfire through the factory. Lennon reminded his companion of Markland's injunction to make sure that they all left the premises. They decided to issue an urgent message over the loudspeaker system for the chief security officer to come to the managing director's office. This official dutifully came in the expectation of being fired himself. Instead, he was surprised to be handed a list of names and told to mark these off as they left through the gates.

The next victim was Gill, the head of management services. His departure was especially ironic as he had prepared or supervised the preparation of the data on the cutting room which, unknown to him, had been used to rationalize his own dismissal. He had, earlier in the week, received a highly confidential handwritten request from Markland to provide him with the ages and lengths of service of those in his department. The implications of this communication were obvious enough, but Gill had not imagined that it was in any way relevant to himself. He uttered some stifled protests to his executioners, but these were dismissed politely, but firmly.

The next victim was the personnel manager. He had to pass a receptionist on his way to the managing director's office.

'I understand,' he said, 'that Mr Markland wishes to see me.'

Automatically she indicated that he was in the boardroom. The personnel manager poked his head around the boardroom door and said to Markland:

'I understand that you wish to see me.'

The reply came back:

'No one here wishes to see you.'

After some further dismissals the telephone operator, who happened to suffer from angina, broke down in tears and had to be replaced by another girl.

The firing day coincided with Prime Minister Heath's resignation and the declaration of a general election. One of the monthly staff went of his own volition to the managing director's office to request leave of absence for the duration of the campaign as he was standing for Parliament. He was told by Markland's secretary that the managing director was too busy to see him at the moment. On his way back to his department he was surprised to hear his name over the factory address system. He returned as instructed to the managing director's office and was there relieved of his duties permanently.

One of the last of the monthly staff to be dismissed was the chief maintenance engineer. He had become very disenchanted with the company and quite openly expressed his contempt for its senior management in most uncompromising terms. He opened the door of the managing director's office and said while he still stood in the corridor:

'How much and when?'

'£950 and now', Palmer replied.

While these events were in progress Johnson received a telephone call from Smith in London who wanted an assurance that the firings had started at Tufted. After receiving this assurance he hurried downstairs to the hotel lounge where several salesmen were waiting. He asked them to hand over their car keys and then gave them their letters of dismissal and cheques. He explained the reasons for the dismissals and wished them success in the future. As they left he handed them amounts of cash exactly calculated to pay for their train journeys home. He would, he explained, settle up with the hotel management. In disgust one of the salesmen cursed and threw the train fare back at Smith.

After two hours Markland received a message from Lennon and Palmer that their mission had been accomplished. He had lectured those in the boardroom about the state of the company and had eventually disclosed that there would have to be certain staff reductions. He indicated that he had arranged a staff conference for them the following week. Residential accommodation in North Yorkshire had, he said, already been booked. More by tone and gesture than words, he indicated to them that they were not allowed to be excused during his talk. At its conclusion most of them were forced to charge down the corridor in search of urgent relief.

The member of staff who earlier had had a conversation with a woman colleague stayed a moment.

'Are you Johnson?', he asked.

After receiving confirmation he enquired:

'Are the people who were in this room being made redundant?'

Birtwhistle had been charged with the duty of dismissing two of the monthly staff at the mill in Cleckheaton. One of these, an inspector, had refused to accept this and indicated that he would not leave unless personally fired by the managing director. Arrangements were therefore made for this to be done immediately after lunch.

At 2.20 in the afternoon the redundancy consultations with the shop stewards and trade union officials took place as scheduled. The officials representing the staff unions arrived, but the local secretary of the relevant manual workers' union failed to appear.

The official representing the supervisors' union at once asked for a list of names of those staff who were to be made redundant. The official from the clerks' union gasped in astonishment when he saw the name of the personnel manager. His colleague from the other union indicated that this document should not be discussed in the corridor and led the way into the boardroom. The officials presented a united front and asked what criteria had been used to select those who would be made redundant.

Markland replied that the company had applied the first in and last out principle. This was rejected by the officials who insisted that non-unionists should be the first to go. Markland and Johnson confessed that they did not actually know who were union members. Johnson was sent out to fetch the shop stewards so that this could be established.

The stewards at once revealed the horrible fact that most of those on the lists were already outside the gates. This put the officials into a hopeless negotiating position. They protested that they had been tricked into believing that these discussions were to be prior to the actual dismissals.

After their anger had abated somewhat it became obvious that most of the redundancies among the monthly staff were not directly related to the closure of the cutting room. It was, for instance, hardly feasible to argue that the dismissal of the personnel manager and many others was a direct outcome of the closure of the cut lengths service. However, the officials were not prepared to concern themselves with these individuals as they were not members of either of their organizions.

They continued, however, to protest that some of their members had been dismissed in grades where non-unionists remained in employment. Markland expressed sympathy with this view, but indicated that it was not practical to attempt to sack any of those remaining in order that certain union members could be reinstated. This was accepted regretfully by the officials, but they continued to argue in respect of the fire and safety officer. He was, they pointed out, a member of the supervisors' union, and his dismissal, they asserted, could not be justified as caused by the closure of the cutting room. Markland felt himself cornered on this particular point and he reluctantly agreed to reinstatement.

After the meeting ended Markland remarked bitterly to Johnson about this reversal. He instructed him to make sure that the fire and safety officer did not have an office or any duties to perform after re-engagement. Subsequently, Johnson failed to carry out these instructions. Before Markland disappeared into his office he fired the following passing shot at Johnson:

'Was that just rattle, rattle?'

Late that afternoon Lennon went to the cutting room and informed the day shift that they would be laid off progressively over the next six months. Palmer and Muldoon, at the same time, also broke the news to several members of the weekly staff. About seventy employees had been fired by the time the factory hooter sounded that evening.

14
A breakdown of taboos

Markland keeps his own council

Markland was very secretive, and he was especially inclined to be so when he contemplated doing something out of the ordinary. He had not consulted his advisers about the desirability of holding the week-end conference of the operating board at Middlesbrough. On that occasion his instincts told him that they would have been highly critical of the whole idea. The apparent success of this conference seemed to confirm to him the wisdom of acting on his instincts. He believed that the redundancy would be sure to have a depressing effect on the remaining staff. Their morale, he thought, could be restored if the team spirit which now seemed to permeate the operating board could be transmitted to them. A further conference seemed to him to be the ideal way of communicating this enthusiasm and the new product strategy to the monthly staff. They, in turn, would be able to relay this to more subordinate staff at Tufted after their return to the factories. If he had discussed this scheme with his advisers, then its inherent absurdity would have been immediately exposed. Like many other chief executives Markland tended to eschew advice when he most needed it.

A few days before the redundancy occurred he booked accommodation for the entire operating board plus thirty of the monthly staff at Astwell Hall. This establishment was at Great Ayton on the edge of the Yorkshire Moors. It normally catered for outward bound type activities, and was much used by para military youth organizations and, occasionally, by companies for gatherings of their craft apprentices. The furnishings and appointments at Astwell Hall were spartan, and the food it provided was nourishing, if unimaginative. Markland had some kind of family connection with the place.

He went to enormous trouble to arrange accommodation in a way calculated to engender *esprit de corps* between directors and directed. Each director was to share a dormitory with up to three of their subordinates. These arrangements were to symbolize a new togetherness and emphasize the fact that they were all in the same boat.

On the day before the redundancy Markland had briefly informed the board that a conference had been arranged and instructed them to keep the following Thursday and Friday free for this purpose. The managing director announced the conference to the monthly staff in the boardroom on the day of the redundancy itself.

On the following Monday he briefed Leyland on the arrangements. He instructed him to prepare an agenda so that each director would have time to explain the implications of the new policy as it affected their respective departments. Leyland was told that it was essential that everyone should be conveyed to Astwell Hall in company cars. Markland and Leyland were to travel in Johnson's car. These travelling arrangements were designed to conceal or minimize the cost of the whole operation.

Shortly after this interview concluded, Johnson was summoned. He was told:

'Astwell Hall is unlicensed and I want you to arrange for a free bar to be set up.'

Johnson enquired about the variety and quantity of drink required, and Markland replied by mumbling something about beer and whisky. After a few seconds hesitation he added:

'Why don't you delegate to Flowerdew, he used to be a quarter-master sergeant you know.'

Johnson had been given the job of looking after what remained of management services and personnel. Flowerdew, who was canteen manager, came within the ambit of the latter department. Within a few hours Flowerdew presented his new boss with a number of invoices for signing.

On Tuesday, Markland's secretary telephoned Gray to tell him of the conference. She added that Markland was not available at the moment, but hoped very much that Gray would be able to attend.

Gray's journey and arrival

Gray had much further to travel than anyone else, and as often happens in such cases he was first to arrive. He chose to go by rail as the weather was very inclement. A chilling wind and driving sleet greeted him as he disembarked at Great Ayton station. He looked about in vain for a taxi, and asked a passing lady the way to Astwell Hall. She looked thoughtful, so Gray volunteered the information that Astwell Hall was an hotel.

'There isn't an hotel here by that name.'

After a moment she added:

'If you're stuck you might try the Red Lion. They sometimes take guests.'

134

Gray thanked her and retraced his steps to the booking hall. There a porter told him:

'Thou'll want the boy scout hostel. Take left turning under bridge. Astwell Hall is about a mile up Moorside Road. It stands among trees just after crossroads.'

Gray started the steady climb, and by the time he reached a sign which read 'Astwell Hall' he was thankful that he was travelling light. He proceeded up a long avenue flanked by trees on either side. When he emerged at the rear of what seemed to be a large deserted house the light had almost faded. The thought that Markland had played a huge practical joke on him crossed his mind. He recalled that the now managing director had shown a considerable talent for that sort of thing when a student. After what seemed like an eternity his knock was answered by a light appearing at the far end of the passage and the door was opened by an elderly gentleman who introduced himself as 'Colonel Franks'. After welcoming his visitor the colonel consulted a chart on the wall and said:

'I will show you to your room. I see you will be sharing with Mr Leyland and Mr Johnson.'

This slightly shocked Gray and his embarrassment was intensified by the appearance of the room itself. It was furnished in a highly functional manner. It contained three beds which were very narrow and had striped mattresses. At the foot of each, bedclothes were folded in squares. He decided to assume possession of the bed nearest the window as it appeared to be the least intimate of the three. He was reassured to some extent by the fact that he had packed some moderately conservative underpants. After a few minutes a call of nature obliged him to explore the corridor outside. He discovered a communal wash-house a few doors away. This contained a veritable battery of water closets which were separated from the main compartment and each other by flimsy partitions. The comedy of the situation seized him and he found himself laughing aloud. His amusement was heightened downstairs when he noticed that the resident directors had been allocated rooms with subordinate staff. Markland, he noted, had a private apartment.

In the sitting room he found a black and white television set which seemed to be about the only concession to modern living in the place. He turned on *Look North* and almost immediately noticed that the sideboard was packed full of drink. After pouring himself a pint of beer he began to feel decidedly more at home.

Gammage was the first of the directors to arrive. The next was Lennon and by this time the sitting room was quite full of staff happily helping themselves to the bountiful provisions contained in the sideboard. Gray challenged all comers to a game of table tennis in the adjoining room. Partnered by the product manager he defeated Gammage and Lennon easily. The atmosphere became almost party-like as more and more drink was consumed. The victorious partnership continued to beat off challengers until Lennon who had left the room shortly after his game, re-entered and took Gray aside to speak privately. His expression had undergone a transformation; the earlier light-heartedness had given way to a grimly serious look:

'Tenniswood and Palmer think that this place is a disgrace and an insult to them as directors,' he said. 'What the hell are we supposed to do? I've not got a towel and I don't think anyone else has either. Have you seen the bloody dining room? It's terrible. Just rough tables and narrow benches. What does David think he's playing at? This is like a bloody Borstal.'

Gray replied:

'Well, it isn't the Ritz, but what's biting you all of a sudden? You were enjoying yourself a short while ago. Just look into the sitting room. They all look perfectly happy to me. Speaking for myself I think that this place has a lot of advantages over fancy hotels.'

Lennon was too serious to be put off by this lighthearted reply and he continued to labour the point about the lack of towels. Gray said:

'I think you're getting the whole thing out of proportion. As for towels, I suggest that we use our pillow cases.'

Lennon left but returned shortly afterwards to inform Gray that the directors found the situation intolerable and were not prepared to remain at Astwell Hall under any circumstances.

'All right, Stuart, but you know as well as I do that it wasn't my idea to come here. I must admit the facilities here came as a bit of a shock to me, but I've been in worse places, and it's only for a couple of nights.'

'It's not so bad for you, George. You're sharing with Howard and Jack. It's great for Markland. He's got the best room in the house all to his bloody self. We've got to share with the monthly staff. How do you think we feel about that?'

'I can see you're not too pleased.'

'What do you mean, I'm not too pleased? In the name of bloody hell, I'm not too pleased.'

'OK, Stuart, but what do you think I can do about it?'

Lennon paused, shrugged his shoulders, and Gray continued:

'I'm not all that clear as to why you've come to me to complain. I'm not even on the full-time staff, let alone a director.'

'You seem to be the only person here who has David's confidence. I'm hoping you can make him see sense.'

'I still think you're overreacting, but I'll see him as soon as he comes and explain the position.'

'It's about bloody time he was here if you ask me.'

'Yes, I can't think what's keeping him.'

'Nothing's keeping him. He does this sort of thing on purpose. He's always buggering us about and treating us like kids.'

Confrontation

Markland had been delayed at the Leeds factory by some urgent telephone calls from the deputy chairman. Johnson drove fast in an attempt to make up for lost time, but they were further delayed by a stop at an attractive pub which had caught the managing director's eye. Over several pints of beer Markland confided to his companions that Astwell Hall was somewhat lacking in amenities. He said:

'It's a bit austere and there isn't any central heating.'

They dismissed these worries as mere trifles and dutifully reassured him that any misgivings about minor inconveniences were entirely misplaced. Leyland even went as far as indicating that a bit of austerity might do everyone a lot of good by helping to induce a greater sense of realism.

The three were in high spirits by the time they arrived at Astwell Hall. Johnson had a ready wit but was, on occasion, rather tactless. As soon as he came through the door into the sitting room he issued the following invitation in a loud voice:

'Anyone for ping pong?'

Gray took Markland aside and left the two newcomers to find their own way to the dormitory.

The two immediately recognized Gray's belongings on the made-up bed near the window. Markland's reservations about the place did not prepare them fully for the circumstances in which they now found themselves.

'I see,' Leyland said, 'that George has grabbed the best bed; he certainly isn't slow at exploiting any fringe benefits that are going.'

At that they both fell about with laughter. After they had recovered somewhat Johnson said:

'You've got to hand it to David. He's got the cheek of the devil bringing people to a place like this.'

For quite a while Johnson had been stifling an urge within his bowels and he sought relief in the communal wash-house down the corridor while his companion made up a bed. Johnson's reverie was disturbed by Lennon's voice which floated over the partition.

'Is that you, Howard?' he asked.

After confirmation he told Johnson to come to Markland's room as soon as possible.

In the meantime Gray had explained the situation to the managing director. He said:

'At first everyone seemed to be quite happy, but then Lennon came to me to complain about the lack of amenities here. He said that Tenniswood and Palmer were not prepared to stay here under any circumstances. I agreed that this place isn't the Ritz, but I took the line that they ought to swallow their pride. The main practical problem is the absence of towels. I've suggested that they could use their pillow cases. There's no doubt, that some of the directors, at least, feel very put out.'

At that moment there was a loud knock on the door, and the resident directors with Muldoon entered. Palmer addressed Markland who was pacing up and down in front of the fireplace. The marketing director looked very worried and claimed to be speaking on behalf of the whole deputation. At first he spoke in a fairly restrained way but he began to lose control of himself as his emotions took over. Suddenly Gray, who was the only seated person, interrupted this tirade. He argued that it was necessary to consider matters more dispassionately, and suggested that someone should fetch Johnson and Leyland so that their views could be considered.

By the time that Lennon returned with Leyland, Birtwhistle was shouting at the top of his voice. He screamed at Markland:

'I'm not going to be treated like a boy scout. We'll be a bloody laughing stock back at the factory. What the hell do you think those blokes out there think? They must think we're bloody daft.'

At that moment Johnson entered. Birtwhistle stopped, and looked at him.

'They think we've all gone bloody daft,' he repeated for Johnson's benefit.

Markland stood rigidly, his face contorted with subdued rage and incomprehension. For the first time since he had joined the company Johnson saw him in a situation he could not control. Birtwhistle broke the silence again repeating:

'We'll be laughing stocks when we get back. You can't make us stay in this place—we're supposed to be directors.'

Markland paused for a moment and then looked across the room to Johnson.

'What do you think, Howard?', he asked.

Johnson was also in a state of some confusion; he could see that Birtwhistle was very angry, and he could tell from the other faces around the room that most people supported him. He didn't know what to do or say. At length he decided that he had to support Markland and so he said:

'I've only just arrived, but it doesn't seem all that bad to me.'

Birtwhistle interjected a snort of dissension, but Johnson continued:

'I think it might all look very different in the morning.'

The directors indicated by the expression on their faces that they disagreed and Lennon said:

'I'm a director and I expect to be treated as such—I don't think directors should be asked to stay in a slum like this.'

Markland turned to Gray; Gray could see that he had lost control and that he had to take over. In a calm and restrained voice he said:

'The place is good enough for me, but I can see that the strength of feeling in this room is very high and I think that we should try to book an hotel in the area. It's very late, but we might be able to do this if we get a move on.'

At once Palmer volunteered to do this as he claimed to have a detailed knowledge of the locality.

The meeting disbanded and for a while Gray was left alone with Markland. In a half hour or so Palmer joined them with the news that he had succeeded in booking accommodation at an hotel in Saltburn. However, he added that the hotel would be unable to provide food so late in the evening for such a large party. Gray reconvened the meeting and all the directors showed that they were very anxious to depart. The consultant told them:

'Howard has just pointed out to me that several of the monthly staff have started eating. I think we should join them. The hotel can't feed us tonight. I'm very hungry for one, and it's bloody absurd not to eat the food that has been prepared.'

Lennon immediately protested in a loud voice.

'I'd prefer to starve than eat in a filthy hole like this.'

The other directors showed by their expressions that they were of the same mind. Palmer asked Gray if he should try to make some arrangements with a restaurant. A few minutes later he returned and announced that a café within walking distance of the hotel had agreed to serve meals. Later it was discovered that its proprietor had persuaded his staff to stay by offering them double pay. Gray remained in command of the situation and raised the question of who was going to have the difficult task of informing Colonel Franks. He looked at Markland and saw that he was completely spent. No one volunteered so he said:

'I think that I had better see to it myself.'

He found the colonel superintending the dining room. Already

139

several of the monthly staff had started on the main course. Gray saw that they seemed to be enjoying themselves and were helping themselves to the wine which was provided in generous amounts. The colonel greeted him in a friendly way, but immediately began to look alarmed when Gray said:

'We're having a spot of trouble with the directors. They don't feel that it's possible for them to stay here—so we are all leaving immediately. I'm very sorry about this, but there's nothing I, or anyone else, can do about it.'

For a second or two the colonel was too shocked to reply, but he then said:

'I know it's not a first class hotel, but the accommodation is adequate, the place is clean, and the food is good and wholesome. Major Markland knew that before he came. If that's the problem why did he think of coming here in the first place? What exactly is the complaint?'

'I can't go into details, Colonel, but they're used to staying in good hotels. They think that their status entitles them to that sort of treatment.'

'Why did you come and tell me this? Why didn't Major Markland come and tell me himself?'

'I'm afraid, he's got rather a lot on his plate at the moment, Colonel.'

'There's no excuse; he had a duty to come and see me personally to explain the matter.'

'I'm sorry, Colonel, but there's nothing I, or anyone else, can do to change matters.'

He turned to the staff who had already begun their dinners and said loudly:

'We're leaving at once. You've got to go and get your things from your rooms now. We're moving into an hotel at Saltburn. Brian Palmer will be at the door to tell you how to get there.'

In disbelief the colonel turned to him and said:

'Surely you are not leaving before you eat the food we've prepared. There's nothing wrong with it. It will all go to waste. This is ridiculous.'

'You're right, but I've no choice, I'm sorry, Colonel.'

'I know you are, Mr Gray. You've got your job to do. I can appreciate that, but I don't see why you've got to do Major Markland's as well.'

He walked away muttering almost to himself:

'It was the least that a gentleman could have done.'

When Gray returned he found Markland still standing motionless, and almost expressionless, in front of the fireplace.

'I've broken the news to Colonel Franks. He took it very badly. I did my best, but he still thinks you should have told him yourself.'

In a tired voice Markland said:

'Thanks, George. He's right, of course, but I couldn't face him right now.'

Gray sat down in the armchair and said simply:

'I know.'

For a minute or two there was silence.

Suddenly, the door was flung violently open and Birtwhistle rushed in gleaming with rage.

'What is it now?', Markland said wearily.

'What is it now? I'll tell you what it is. I've just had about as much of you as I can stand.'

Birtwhistle blurted these words out between gasps, as this normally reticent director attempted to express his thoughts. His West Riding accent came through much stronger than usual; it was clear that he was finding it difficult to hold himself back from physically assaulting Markland. His diatribe was interrupted by Johnson who entered the room. Birtwhistle looked at the newcomer and then back to Markland.

'I'm not afraid to say it in front of him,' he said indicating Johnson.

'It's obvious to everyone that he and Jack are executive material. They wouldn't be here unless you intended to put them on the board. How do you think the rest of us feel?'

The question was rhetorical and Birtwhistle did not pause for reply.

'Can't you see what you're doing to people? Stuart has been waiting to be chopped off at the knees ever since Howard came. If you intend to get rid of him why in God's name don't you do it? You're driving us mad.'

Markland stood transfixed before the fireplace. After a moment's silence Gray stood up and in a matter of fact tone said:

'If we're going to Saltburn then I think that it's time we went.'

On his way to his room Johnson passed two of the monthly staff who had been assigned to him after the redundancy. One of them made a slight greeting as he approached and the other said:

'Fred and I don't think that we should be absent from the factory for two days. We're engineers and it's our job to keep it running.'

Johnson did not feel like arguing, but he felt obliged to say something.

'This conference,' he said, 'is being held to discuss company policy—don't you think that you are part of the company?'

The two were outraged by this reply and Fred said:

'He's just said we're not company men.'

141

Johnson tried to point out that this was not the meaning of his remarks, but his defence fell on deaf ears. As he left, he heard them complaining loudly to other members of staff about the insult that they had just received.

Johnson, Leyland, and Gray were the last, or almost the last, to leave Astwell Hall. Johnson looked up from the driver's seat and saw Markland's forlorn figure silhouetted in the entrance hall. He called out and Markland slowly made his way to the waiting car. Gray said:

'He's taken it badly. We must stand by him.'

By the time Markland arrived at the hotel in Saltburn Palmer had already announced that the cocktail bar would be free to all 'delegates'. Later Markland himself added that meals and drinks at the restaurant were also on the company. In spite of this corporate generosity the atmosphere at the restaurant remained tense. After about half an hour the subdued conversation over tables was shattered by the product manager who began to berate Markland. He accused his patron (this manager had been personally recruited by Markland) of callous indifference to the feelings and interests of others. He described the redundancy as completely unnecessary and condemned the way in which it was handled, in bitter terms. The managing director suddenly stood up in the middle of this tirade and without saying anything returned to the hotel.

For a while the conversation at the restaurant became artificially polite, but gradually inhibitions were broken down under the combined influence of alcohol and the tension induced by earlier events. Several people began to abuse each other, and the normal respect which subordinates exhibit towards their superiors was cast aside. Gradually, the staff returned to the hotel. Several of them seemed then to be suffering from emotional exhaustion.

On arrival at the hotel Smith realized that he had left a coat and some other belongings at the restaurant. He asked Gray to accompany him back to the restaurant. Gray found that he had to guide his companion back over unlit roads and help him up steps. He was astonished by Smith's physical frailty. In the boardroom Smith gave the appearance of self-sufficiency and the thought occurred to him that Smith must have gone to great lengths to conceal his infirmities by such things as well cut and padded suits.

When Gray returned to the hotel he found an urgent message awaiting him, to go immediately to Markland's room. He found the managing director in a highly agitated state. Markland said:

'What's the use of it all? Why should I go through this for those bastards? They aren't worth it. I don't get much more than you do. By the time the tax people have finished with me I'm hardly better off than you are. I work all hours of the day and night for what? Just to be abused by that lot.'

Gray signalled his agreement and asked simply:

'What do you intend to do?'

Markland replied:

'Can't you get me a job at the college. With what I could earn on the side I would be nearly as well off as I am now. I feel I need to take things easier. It's not worth enduring the kind of pressure that I've been subjected to for peanuts.'

His companion continued:

'I wish I could get you a job, but I'm only a lecturer. I'm a nobody at the college. I've had my work cut out just to survive myself. I can't get promotion for myself let alone get a job for you.'

Almost desperately Markland said:

'I'm sure you can do something if you try. You could at least fix me up with a lecture series.'

Before Gray could reply he added:

'Would it help, if I put up some money to finance a bit of research?'

'What do you have in mind, David?'

'Well, I could get Tufted to sponsor some market research or something useless like that.'

'I'm sure that would help a lot. If you were a success as a visiting lecturer I think you might be wangled on to the full-time staff. I'll take soundings as soon as I get back. I'm sure if the scheme went ahead that the college could be persuaded to give you an impressive title like "Visiting Fellow". That costs nothing.'

'That sounds great, George. A title like that on an application form would look really good. I'm sure that it would help me get a job elsewhere if I can't get on the full-time staff at the college. If you bring this off I'll see that you get a copper-bottomed contract. I'll see that your salary's increased by £1000. You'll be at Tufted long after I've left.'

Although by now it was three in the morning he commanded Gray to accompany him to the room in which Johnson and Leyland were sleeping. These two were somewhat bewildered by the arrival of a deputation in the early hours. After some ribald remarks Markland said:

'Be at my room at a quarter to eight so that we can plan our strategy for the morrow.'

In the morning Johnson and Leyland dutifully arrived in compliance with this instruction, but Markland seemed to have recovered his spirits and he said:

'The best thing you two can do is get yourselves a good breakfast.'

Gray overslept and failed to arrive at the managing director's room at the appointed time. In fact, he was last down to breakfast.

Markland opened proceedings confidently, he said:

'I think we must put the events of yesterday behind us. We are here to discuss the future of the company.'

He continued by outlining the new product strategy which would, he contended, lay the foundation of future profitability and enable them all to face the forthcoming year in an optimistic spirit.

The rest of the morning passed without particular incident as Markland called upon the various directors to explain how the new policy would be implemented in their respective areas. The directors responded by giving shortened versions of the speeches which they had made at Middlesbrough.

Markland decided for some unexplained reason that everyone should take an extended lunch break. Most of the company took the opportunity of taking a walk on the beach. On that day the sun shone pleasantly with the promise of future warmth. Gray felt too exhausted to join Johnson and Leyland on the beach. Instead, he retired to his room and managed to snatch a few moments of fitful sleep. By the time he arrived at the conference room Birtwhistle was addressing the assembly. Unlike the other directors he spoke at inordinate length. Much to Gray's dismay he produced the same collection of samples which he had displayed at Middlesbrough, and he described their properties in painful detail. Gray grew angrier and angrier. He looked about him and saw that the members of the operating board seemed to be indifferent to the futility and waste of time embodied in the proceedings. Markland had asked him to address the meeting on the problems of industrial relations. He began to look anxiously at the clock and became keenly aware that he might not be able to do this and catch the late afternoon train. He had some lectures at college next morning and if he failed to catch that particular train he would miss the connection at Darlington. He tried to catch Markland's eye, but the latter seemed to be completely indifferent to the situation.

He leant over to speak to Johnson:

'You'll have to talk to them about industrial relations if he doesn't finish soon. I've got a train to catch.'

Eventually Birtwhistle finished and Markland asked Gray to speak.

'I've got a train to catch in ten minutes. Like all of you I've endured hour upon hour of boredom and wasted time this afternoon. Why do we talk about trivial things which you all know about? This waste of time is typical of the way in which this company is run. The plain truth is that this company hasn't got a sales policy, a marketing policy, a purchasing policy, or for that matter a policy on anything. The so-called "new product strategy" is nothing more than wishful thinking at the moment. The wages and salary structures are just a mess. They need simplifying. Wage rates between the three factories need bringing into line.'

At that moment a member of the hotel staff entered the room and announced that Mr Gray's taxi was waiting for him. The consultant finished abruptly by saying:

'I'm sorry, but I must go. If you want to discuss industrial relations further I suggest that you ask Mr Johnson to continue.'

The journey to the station was short and gave Gray little time for reflection. He felt angry, bitter, and frustrated. By the time he had boarded the train these feelings had subsided and were replaced with acute embarrassment. He felt a deep sinking sensation in his stomach. He now knew that he had behaved stupidly but, in his confusion, he did not quite see why. The thought crossed his mind that Markland would not wish to see him again. He shrugged his shoulders and thought to himself what the hell does it matter in any case. On the express from Darlington he ordered himself dinner and quickly drank a bottle of wine. In spite of his troubled mind he slept soundly after returning to his compartment. By the time he arrived home he felt much better.

The atmosphere which he left behind him at the hotel was understandably electric. As soon as he had left Markland suggested that the meeting should adjourn so as to take afternoon tea. The consultant had left indicating that Johnson would take over. The latter made up his mind in the break that he would publicly dissociate himself from Gray's remarks. He saw that Smith was white and was actually trembling.

'What right,' Smith said, 'has he got to come here and say things like that.'

Johnson agreed and was surprised when Lennon interrupted:

'You two might not like what he said. You don't like it because it's true. Every damn word of it is true. It's the only bit of truth that's been spoken in this damn conference. I'm pleased he spoke the truth; it's what we need.'

After the interval Markland rose to the occasion; he was at his most eloquent:

'You have all heard what Mr Gray said. It was all perfectly true, but you must not blame yourselves and feel angry. His indictment was not of you. It was an indictment of me. I accept it. I'm responsible as managing director for policy. The lack of it is entirely my responsibility. I'm accountable.'

This statement was greeted with stunned silence. No one said anything and Johnson did not make his intended public statement. The assembly broke up ostensibly to take an early dinner.

Later that evening Smith and Palmer addressed the conference. They were quietly and politely received, but to tell the truth by now no one was really listening.

15

Business as usual: an incipient fourth order

Four months of comparative calm

On their return to Tufted from Astwell Hall the members of the operating board resumed their normal routines as though nothing unusual had occurred. For the moment they seemed to be drained of emotional energy. If there were any plots directed at undermining Markland's position, then they were very well hidden and disguised.

In the four months of comparative, or at least, surface calm which followed, the motto seemed to be 'business as usual'. Day followed day without major incident, and there seemed to be no reason why this state of affairs should not continue more or less indefinitely. However, it is precisely at such times when nothing in particular seems to be happening, that one can observe the mechanisms of power and patronage with more detachment, and at greater leisure.

Johnson finds a niche and becomes a part-time chauffeur

Johnson was put in charge of the works engineers and what remained of personnel and management services. He spent a day or so getting acquainted with those involved and in assigning tasks. Afterwards, he found that he had very little to do. He used to spend a lot of time looking out of the window in his new office; he often wondered what on earth his three predecessors and their several subordinates did to fill in time.

He pondered, also, about why Markland did not claim the company car to which he was entitled. It seemed so inexplicable in view of the evident importance which the managing director attached to status expenditures and conspicuous consumption. Even though he had the services of company chauffeurs at his command there were obviously times when he was inconvenienced by his dependence on others for transport. Gray too was perplexed by this, particularly as he remembered that Markland had, back in his student days, taken much pride in his Morgan. The absence of a car, however, provided him with excuses to seek out others and Johnson, in particular, so as to relieve his isolation. On one occasion, for instance, he summoned him to come urgently to his office over the public address system. He smiled at a breathless Johnson and said:

'Are you especially busy at the moment, Howard?'

'I've got a few things to do, but there's nothing that can't wait for a minute or two.'

'There's a cottage near Ripon that I'd like to look at. Let's go and see it. I'd like a second opinion on it.'

Fringe benefits

Johnson did not obtain his promised Cortina 2000E until well on into the quiet period. Meanwhile, he had to make do with a rather ancient Cortina 1300. He was slightly disappointed that the new car was a rather unappealing shade of blue and not white, as he had ordered.

Leyland was not entitled to a company car under the original terms of his appointment, but after taking charge of production control he took the opportunity of raising the matter with the managing director. Markland demurred slightly, but eventually agreed. He handed a list of models to Leyland and said:

'You can choose any of the models below the line which I've drawn, Jack.'

Leyland, quite naturally, chose the highest ranking of the available models—a Cortina XL. This never arrived and he suffered a rather bigger disappointment than his friend as he was allocated a very shabby Avenger with a high mileage.

These delays and disappointments were a by-product of the cash shortage which afflicted the company. It had been decided to sell company cars to a vehicle rental firm and then to lease them back so as to ease the cash flow problem.

Even the factory at Leeds had been sold and leased back, and shortly afterwards this procedure was repeated with the machinery in all three factories. This strategy was also followed in other parts of Total and, as a result, a massive set of bills was created which had to be paid regularly. This, of course, served to intensify cash flow difficulties. Financial accountants had to resort to more and more desperate expedients just so that Total could remain afloat. The whole edifice was balanced on a knife edge.

Gray comes under the spell of the fourth order

Markland enjoyed not paying accounts. He thought it was only common sense to withhold payment until the last possible moment. He was not therefore particularly concerned when Gray mentioned that he had not received his fees from Muldoon. It was a situation which he savoured; the delays in payment served to underline the fact that the consultant was dependent on him.

Gray adapted himself to this circumstance by maximizing his expenses which were paid out of petty cash on a visit-by-visit basis. After three months of non-payment and polite enquiry he decided to have a showdown with Markland. He said:

'Look, David, I don't want to be unpleasant, but I'm sick and tired of coming here without payment. I'm not swallowing any more of Muldoon's excuses. He's just mucking me about for the sheer hell of it. We're going to sort it out here and now. I'm not leaving this office until I'm paid.'

'Damn his eyes. I told him to see to it weeks ago. I'm sorry about this, George.'

With that the managing director picked up the telephone and ordered Muldoon's deputy to come to his office immediately. Within minutes this accountant had made out a cheque payable to Gray which completely cleared the arrears. As he handed it over he said:

'Will it be all right, Sir, if from now on I make out a cheque for the required amount on the last Friday of each month.'

'That's fine.'

'Would you like it posted to the business school or to your home address, Sir?'

'My home address would be much more convenient, thank you.'

Now that fees began to supplement expenses he began to feel, for the first time in his life, well off. It was a new experience for him to go about with pockets bulging with money. It was a novelty for him to be able to make even quite substantial purchases without counting the cost.

He even began to forego, once a week, the profitable mileage allowance and treat himself to the luxury of the early morning express to Leeds. After a few journeys he got to know the regular dining car attendant and his generous, but calculated tips, assured him of preferential treatment. He enjoyed really substantial breakfasts and always had as many cups of coffee as he desired without having to pay any additional charge. At Leeds, his pride, and his growing sense of his own importance were confirmed by a company chauffeur who dutifully awaited his arrival at the main entrance to the station. The process of his absorption into the fourth order was well advanced, but not, as yet, complete. He still felt obliged to sit beside the chauffeur rather than at the rear. Often he would have preferred it otherwise as he found conversation with the chauffeur tiresome in the extreme.

Some of his ingrained habits, however, proved impossible or difficult to break. For example, he continued to claim at the first class rate although he chose to travel second class. In spite of residual working class touches of this kind, the fact of his assimilation into the fourth order was plain for everyone to see. He began to talk a lot more about business topics in general and about his consultancy in particular. His established friends did not find this attractive—to them he was fast becoming an insufferable bore.

His relationship with Lennon became more and more firmly established. In a moment of disloyalty to Markland he confessed:

'I suppose you know, Stuart, that David wanted to get rid of you?'

'I gathered as much, but I couldn't quite make out why he didn't see it through.'

'As a matter of fact David and I talked about you. I defended you, as did Howard, even though David brought him in as your replacement.'

'I didn't know that.'

'I must confess, Stuart, I didn't know much about you at the time, but I just couldn't see you as a threat to David. I thought he ought to aim at other targets rather than waste ammunition on you.'

Lennon, was among other things, responsible for the garage and as a result a great amount of attention was lavished on Gray's car. However, in spite of this care which included an oil change on almost every visit the effects of hard unrelenting motorway driving were impairing the performance of its small engine. The consultant decided to invest some of his newly acquired wealth into a much more powerful and luxurious car. When he first drove this limousine into Tufted it excited much attention and comment. Lennon came out of the boardroom especially to see it. He remarked:

'That's a nice looking car you've got there, George. These Volvos have a lot of good engineering in them.'

'Yes, Stuart. I'm pleased with it. It goes like a bomb. I've cut a half hour off the journey without pushing it.'

'Small cars, like that old Escort of yours, aren't a good idea. They're a false economy. These are so much more comfortable and quieter. They're made for blasting up the motorway.'

'I'm a bit concerned about this back tyre, it looks a bit on the thin side to me. I'd hate to have a blow-out on the motorway.'

'Yes, it looks a bit worn. I change mine after every ten thousand even if they seem OK. You can't be too careful about tyres. Leave the keys with me and I'll get the transport manager to take it into the garage.'

Later that day both of them went over to the garage. Lennon winked at him as the transport manager came across and explained:

'I'm sorry it's so late, but we didn't have any of this size in stock so

150

we sent a van into town for some. We've given it a good going over, and road tested it. It's in tip top condition.'

Gray was astonished to see that his car had been fitted with four new radials.

He was grateful that Lennon was joining him for dinner at the motel that night. He disliked the anonymity of the place and the slick superficial salesmen who seemed to form the basis of its clientele. Recently, Johnson had been inviting him to stay the odd night or two at the house he had rent free from Tufted. Gray really appreciated these gestures. Indeed, rather than spend a night at the motel or some other faceless place, he often chose to drive the 170 miles each way to Leeds in a day.

Feathering nests

The carpets in Gray's house were ill assorted and, for the most part, badly worn. He took advantage of the executive purchasing scheme which allowed him to obtain carpet at ex-work prices minus a substantial discount. He decided to purchase enough of Tufted's most luxurious standard product—a deep shag made of trilobal nylon filament with a resplendent sheen—to carpet the whole of his downstairs. When the consignment arrived he noticed immediately that it had a number of defects, and with the help of his wife he rolled it out on the lawn. To their dismay they saw two big holes, one of which was a good yard wide. He said:

'It's obvious that someone at Tufted must dislike me.'

On his next visit to Tufted Lennon told him:

'You're silly to order things through Markland. I'll see to it myself.'

Within a few days a replacement arrived and Gray telephoned Lennon.

'Thanks, Stuart. The carpet you sent is perfect.'

'Oh, that's all right George. It should be OK it's grade A. I inspected it myself and saw that it was dispatched properly. The trouble with David is that he hands an invoice or something to someone in the belief that things take care of themselves. I've not been able to find out who messed you about, but if I do, I'll have the bugger's guts for garters.'

'I'm coming up to Leeds tomorrow. Why don't we have lunch at the pub?'

'That's a good idea.'

Johnson was less successful than Gray in the matter of cars, but he easily out did him so far as carpets were concerned. Birtwhistle designed a deep pile carpet of pure wool to meet his requirements and personally superintended its production. In order to ensure cus-

151

tomer satisfaction he even invited Johnson's wife to the mill to make sure that it also met with her approval.

Johnson established a telephone relationship with the sales director of one of Total's furniture manufacturing subsidiaries. His wife was attracted by some dining room furniture and a sideboard which appeared in that company's catalogue. Apologetically, his contact told him that these items had been withdrawn, but added that there was a possible way around this problem. He would see that these items were manufactured specially, provided Johnson could arrange for him to have the carpet from an exhibition stand. Both were to obtain their wares at substantial discounts—it clinched the deal.

Johnson and Lennon usually had a quick pint together after work, in a pub outside the factory gates. There was in Johnson a residual streak of puritanism, and he was shocked when Lennon and Gray went to the pub after taking lunch in the boardroom. He did, once, join them to have lunch there rather than in the boardroom but that was, to his way of thinking, something totally different. The two of them were on one occasion having their evening drink together when a company chauffeur entered. Lennon got up and said:

'What are you having Bill?'

When the chauffeur left Johnson said:

'The crafty old sod.'

'What do you mean?'

'He's on overtime.'

'I don't quite follow you.'

'He drives David home. Comes in here for a few jars before going back into the factory to clock out. You'd think he'd stop off and have one on the other side of town wouldn't you?'

In disbelief Lennon ran to the door and saw the chauffeur's car disappearing into the factory. He got to work very early next morning and checked the offending chauffeur's clock card. He decided that he was going to put a stop to that sort of caper once and for all. He transferred chauffeurs and the drivers of light vans from day shift to double day shift. At a stroke he drastically curtailed their scope to work overtime.

Moonlighting

Gray was not the only moonlighter at Tufted. Late one Monday afternoon, Johnson was summoned to Markland's office. After the usual pleasantries, Markland said:

'I've got a bit of a problem; I'm due to give a day's lecture on corporate planning in London on Wednesday and the chairman wants me to go to a meeting at St Albans.'

After a pause, he went on:

'Will you do the lecture for me?'

Johnson knew nothing of the subject matter of corporate planning. He knew, of course, of the existence of such a function, and was well aware of its ostensible purpose, but he knew nothing of any techniques or methodology which might form the basis of a day's lecture. He hesitated for some moments and said:

'I'd like to help, David, but I know nothing about it.'

'There's nothing to know. I've got all the slides here; they're in sequence, all you do is show the slides and waffle on a bit about them.'

Johnson was still troubled; he had never lectured on a course in his life, other than internal ones, and then he had simply been explaining his own work to colleagues.

'I don't think I could do it, David.'

'Of course you can. There's fifty quid in it for you. Look, all you have to do is go through these slides, talk a bit about generalities and then put them in syndicates for a case study. If you like, we'll get Jack to go down and give them a lecture on forecasting—that should kill a couple of hours.'

Johnson could see that he was not being offered a choice, and the prospect of an extra fifty pounds helped to tip the balance.

Markland pressed home his advantage:

'I'll tell you what, the course goes on for three days, and I'll be there on Thursday and Friday. Why don't you stay for the whole time. Bring your wife up and we'll have an evening on the town.'

Without waiting for him to agree, he lifted the telephone and spoke to his secretary:

'Book a double room for Mr and Mrs Johnson at the Kensington Close for Tuesday, Wednesday, and Thursday—the bill to be sent direct to me here, and make out a couple of first class warrants and book them seats on the evening pullman tomorrow.'

He beamed at Johnson across the table and added:

'Any other expenses—you can put on a standard form and I'll sign them.'

He handed over a folder—full of slides for an overhead projector, a timetable, and a number of typed sheets stapled together.

'This is the case study; you can start them off on it sometime in the afternoon. Ask them to prepare their answers for Thursday morning—I should be there by then.'

Johnson was about to query the apparent doubt about Markland's arrival on Thursday, but before he could begin, the managing director picked up the telephone and asked his secretary to dial a London number. When he was connected Johnson overheard the one half of the conversation.

'Sorry, Jimmy, I can't make Wednesday, the chairman's called a meeting.'

He winked at Johnson and continued:

'Don't flap, Jimmy, I've got someone else to do it.'

'Yes he's been a corporate planner for five years.'

'Don't worry, Jimmy; his name is "Howard Johnson".'

He covered the mouthpiece and whispered:

'He's a bit of an old woman. He wants to come and see you at the hotel tomorrow evening. Is that OK?'

Johnson nodded and Markland continued:

'That's OK, Jimmy.'

'No make it about nine thirty. He's coming up on the pullman.'

'No, that's all right. He'll see you then, and I'll come down on Wednesday evening.'

Johnson spent most of the Tuesday making notes, looking at the slides and thinking about what to say. The slides seemed to him to be fatuous and showed abstract concepts such as a 'hierarchy of company plans' and a 'forecast of the *status quo*'. One slide headed 'gap analysis' struck him as particularly absurd.

He had butterflies in his stomach before he actually got to the lecture theatre. As he mounted the rostrum and turned to see a mass of serious and expectant faces he was seized by feelings which amounted almost to panic. Fortunately, he did not have to start lecturing immediately as Jimmy, a senior lecturer in business policy at the Polytechnic, was waiting to introduce him. Jimmy said:

'It gives me the greatest pleasure to introduce Howard Johnson to you. He's been in corporate planning for five years. At present, he is senior planning and operations executive at Total Furnishings. Howard Johnson has a deep and thorough knowledge of his subject, and we are indeed fortunate to have his services at such short notice. I am sure that you would wish to join me in welcoming him in the usual manner.'

When the applause subsided, Johnson went to the overhead projector, and after taking a deep gulp of air he launched himself into his presentation. He knew he was talking bilge and was more than relieved to see that his audience was both attentive and uncritical. By the end of the day he felt that he had just earned the easiest fifty pounds in his life.

This lecture was the first of a number of occasions when he found himself earning a little easy money on the side.

154

Rules and regulations

Muldoon interpreted his role as commercial manager very broadly; he was interested in all aspects of company administration from the allocation of office carpeting to the preparation of annual returns. His interest in the minutiae of office life was often found extremely irksome by Johnson. On one occasion, for instance, Johnson had been staring at the carpet in his office. He found its colour and design displeasing in the extreme. In normal circumstances he would have shrugged his shoulders and ignored the offending object, but he was finding it very difficult to fill his time. In the absence of other diversions, he decided to seek out Lennon to choose an alternative.

Lennon was also in a leisurely mood, and he suggested that they should both visit the factory showroom and choose a replacement. While they were there, they could use their time efficiently as Lennon had promised his wife that he would take some pattern books home, for her to choose another design for her mother's lounge. Johnson selected a long-pile cream coloured carpet with dark brown splodges, and Lennon immediately sent instructions to the factory to procure and fit the carpet.

A few days later, Muldoon was in Johnson's office. He could hardly fail to notice the new acquisition. After complimenting Johnson on his taste, he commented that he had not seen the order for this carpet going through the system. With some irritation, Johnson told him that he had not wasted anyone's time by going through internal ordering procedures.

'I arranged it with Stuart, he doesn't need a ton of paper just to deliver an ounce of carpet.'

Muldoon lowered himself into a chair, and began to lecture Johnson on the compelling reasons for following office procedures. He said that there were rules as to how frequently office carpets should be changed; this ensured that there was not too much wastage in this area. There were also rules as to which styles of carpet any class of executive could select. He went on in a confidential tone:

'Actually you are not supposed to choose this range. It's for directors only.'

Johnson was near to boiling point when Muldoon brought out his final objection.

'The real problem is VAT.'

He produced a ball point pen from his top pocket, and looking down at the carpet he began to make notes, he wrote down the style and colour and then looked at Johnson.

'About fifteen square yards, wouldn't you think?'

'I've no bloody idea.'

'Yes, about fifteen square yards I think.'

Muldoon noted this measure, and then started to work out a small sum. He talked to himself as he did it.

'Self supply, has to be at normal out prices, no discounts, that's about £2.17 a square yard, so fifteen times £2.17 is £32.55 so the VAT at twenty-five per cent makes it £8.14 and a bit.'

He looked up at Johnson and with some pride he said:

'We owe the Inland Revenue £8.14 for that little lot, it's self supply, you see, and that makes it liable for VAT.'

He continued in a slightly patronizing tone:

'Don't worry about this one, I'll make out the order and see that it all goes through OK, but do use the system next time.'

When Muldoon had left, Johnson picked up his telephone and dialled Jack Leyland, he recounted the conversation, finishing up by saying:

'You don't know whether to laugh or cry do you?'

One evening about a week later, a bemused carpet fitter from the factory ripped up Johnson's new carpet, and replaced it with an identical piece that he had been given by the stores. When he went back to the stores he said:

'Daftest bloody thing I've ever seen. You sure we had to replace that carpet?'

'Sure, Bill,' said the storeman, 'I've got the order right here, it's signed by Mr Muldoon, you know what he's like when we question his orders.'

Status

In his new role, Johnson was nominally responsible for the allocation of car parking spaces. It was a job that the personnel manager used to do conscientiously every six months or so. The previous allocation had been done before Johnson and Leyland had arrived and, consequently, they did not have spaces allocated to them. It had not been a matter of great concern as they just parked in the nearest untenanted space when they arrived. After the redundancy, there were many spare places, but for some reason unfathomable to Johnson, the old congestion crept back, and even some overspill on to the access roads began to appear.

One morning, Leyland walked into Johnson's office and put a small handwritten note in front of him.

'I found this poked through the window of my car last night.'

It read: 'Please do not park in this RESERVED space'—and was signed by a junior accountant from Muldoon's department.

'Pompous little bastard,' said Johnson, who was somewhat amused by the incident.

'It must be something to do with being an accountant; do you think Muldoon gives them compulsory classes on pomposity in the evening?'

'No, it's part of their ACA exams,' said Leyland.

'Which space was it?' asked Johnson.

Leyland went over to the window, and pointed to a space in the car park.

'It's that one, over in the corner, where I've parked this morning.'

Johnson smiled to himself at this boyish prank of Leyland's, and the next morning, he arrived before Leyland, and despite the availability of more favourable positions, he parked his car in the offending space. For the next week or so, they enjoyed competing to fill the space. The accountant was, habitually, a little later in arriving, and Johnson took to standing at his window to watch the annoyance on his face as he drove around the car park looking for an alternative space.

A few days later, Muldoon arrived in Johnson's office, carrying a plan of the car park.

'The car park allocations are a bit out of date,' he said; 'I thought you might like to reallocate them.'

Johnson tossed the blank plan into his in-tray and said nothing. Muldoon went on:

'I've got a list here of staff entitled to reserved spaces.'

He put the list on Johnson's desk, and disappeared.

Johnson glanced at the list, tossed that too into his in-tray, and forgot about it.

A few days later, Muldoon reappeared in his office.

'Have you done the car park allocations, Howard?'

Johnson indicated that he had not had the time, and added:

'I don't think it's very important, why don't we operate a first come first served system?'

'I've had a little trouble with my staff; I expect them to work late quite frequently, and the following morning I usually allow them to be a little late in, and they find sometimes that they have to park on the road.'

'The extra ten yards walk won't hurt them, it might even do them some good, your department does tend to be a little overweight.'

Muldoon withdrew, but the following morning he was in Johnson's office again.

'I've drafted a plan for the car park, Howard, perhaps you would like to look at it.'

He left the plan on Johnson's desk. It had clearly been a major piece of diplomacy. The space nearest to the entrance was labelled 'managing director', other directors had been allocated the next most favourable positions in strict hierarchical order. After all of the directors' spaces had been allocated, the next best was labelled 'Muldoon' and the next 'Johnson'. A couple of accountants came next, and at the end of the first row was a space labelled 'Leyland'.

Johnson was greatly amused by this little document with all its social undertones, but he still did nothing to implement the scheme.

By the time of the next regular management meeting, he had forgotten all about car parks, and was amazed when Muldoon introduced the subject for discussion. Johnson repeated that he did not see anything wrong in allowing people to park where they liked, but Muldoon countered by arguing fiercely that his staff thought the matter important. Johnson slipped out of the boardroom, and returned seconds later with Muldoon's draft plan. While Muldoon was still talking, he made a couple of adjustments to it. Eventually Johnson said:

'If you feel so strongly about these petty marks of status I've no real objection to publishing this plan.'

He waved the draft plan in front of Muldoon.

'I don't feel strongly about it at all, it's just my staff, and I can see their point.'

'Yes, I agree, we'll use this.'

He tossed the draft plan to Markland's secretary, who was taking notes.

'I've made a couple of small adjustments, but in the main I agree with you.'

He turned to Markland and added:

'All right if your secretary types this up and circulates it?'

'Yes, let's get on with it, I don't call meetings of the board just to discuss car parking.'

When the plan was circulated the next day, Muldoon found, to his chagrin that Johnson had changed Leyland into the space favoured by Muldoon, and Muldoon was relegated to the space he had previously allocated to Leyland.

This incident had a small tailpiece a few months later. Johnson had laughingly told the story to Gammage in a pub one evening. They were both amused at the pricking of Muldoon's pomposity, and Gammage had been previously unaware of the alterations made by Johnson. Gammage was a very junior member of the operating board, and he had often suffered from Muldoon's pomposity. When, one afternoon, he noticed Muldoon's car in a space reserved for directors he immediately went to the receptionist.

'Please ring Mr Muldoon and ask him to remove his car from the directors' car park immediately.'

He then went with Birtwhistle and Leyland to Johnson's office to witness a red-faced and humiliated Muldoon comply with the instruction.

Gray continues to play variations on the same theme

Gray continued to urge Markland to dispense with the services of Muldoon and Palmer, and he repeated his advice about the need to do away with the system of management accounting. On the thirteenth of March he wrote a letter to the managing director which contained the following passages:

▶ I am still extremely concerned about the management accounting system at Tufted, and I am coming to the opinion that most of the operating board now realize that the information produced by the accounts department is worse than useless. The time seems ripe for decisive action.

The overhead recovery data seem especially doubtful. They seem to be based on a series of break even points. For instance, the budget target for each month in respect of Branksome is 18 680. The January accounts show that only 411 sq. yards were in fact produced giving a negative variance of 18 269 sq. yds. This implies that overheads are not being recovered here and this, in turn, implies that a loss is being made on that particular kind of carpet. Again, the underrecovery on Appalachian was even greater because none was actually produced against a budget requirement of 38 000 sq. yds. The budget requirements or break even points seem to be derived from hypothetical data concerning such things as machine speed and material utilization. These data seem to have little relationship to actual performance levels in the workshops. Who actually sets the break even points and what procedure exists for changing these in the light of actual production experience? How are variances expressed in square yards converted into money terms? I cannot get coherent answers to these sort of questions from your commercial manager.

More fundamentally, I cannot for the life of me see how a system of break even points can make sense when one is operating a continuous process with different products going through the same machines. Such production implies that, if one is not making Y, then one is making X. A negative variance in respect of Y is directly responsible for a positive variance for X. Such an accounting system cannot provide meaningful information on anything, and does

159

not fulfil any control or predictive function. In January most of the break even points were not reached because of short-time working and the management accounts point in the general direction of financial information which implies that a substantial loss was made in that month. I can remember saying at Middlesbrough that the firm would be lucky if it was breaking even when others had been talking about current profit. It seems obvious to me that costs were remaining more or less constant when income was falling because of short-time working. One does not need a computer and an elaborate management accounting system to see things like that.

The company would clearly be better off without its present system of management accounting and the overhead costs which that system represents. This is not to say that the company would not benefit from an appropriate system of management accounting, but what that system should be is, in my opinion, something which should be decided by the operating board itself; in no circumstances should it be entrusted to a firm of consultants.

The changes which are being made by the commercial manager are absurd; he simply intends to present the same data in a more summarized form. He still seems to think that the fault lies with others who do not, according to him, appreciate the meaning of the management accounting data currently being produced. In my opinion, he is incapable of anything other than the blind elaboration and application of routines. If this is the case, then it follows that staff changes in the accounts section are a precondition to an effective review of the system of accounting.

I understand that Stuart Lennon has just made a spot check on a row of carpet in the warehouse. He found that out of 2000 rolls 300 were unmentioned on the computer printouts, and that some of these had been ordered as long as six months ago but still remained undispatched. This shop floor information is really alarming in view of the claims concerning the accuracy of the stock control system made by the commercial manager and others.

He found that Markland was becoming even more evasive, and he became increasingly concerned by his failure to make any further changes. He did, however, secure his agreement to undertake a complete review and simplification of the wage structure. He threw himself into this work with considerable enthusiasm, and together with Lennon he began a systematic review. For three months management services had been unable to furnish him with satisfactory bar charts depicting relative earnings. The removal of its head created circumstances in which it was possible to assign a junior work study officer to this task full-time. At first, Muldoon refused to allow him access to information on earnings, but thanks to the intervention of Johnson this resistance was overcome in a few days. In spite of this delay the requisite bar charts were produced in under a fortnight. The co-operation of the unions was sought and obtained, and a series of negotiations were undertaken which culminated in flat rates of payment throughout the three factories plus an agreement on differentials between hourly paid operators and their weekly paid supervision. The company also withdrew from the British Textile Employers' Association in order to avoid the constraints implied by national agreements. As a result of these changes, circumstances were created where it was possible for the company to negotiate a single increase with the unions at the annual wage review. The prior understanding on differentials enabled this single rate to be applied throughout the shop floor in the three factories.

After this, Gray turned his attention to the monthly staff. There had been no policy for setting monthly staff salaries, and each departmental head had decided the pay of his subordinates unilaterally. Each director was asked to grade his subordinates in terms of their relative responsibilities. Gray and Lennon drew these together on a single organization chart and attached to them the actual earnings of the individuals concerned. The results were startling. There was little relation between actual pay and responsibility, and there was little parity of pay between comparable jobs done in different departments. Tenniswood was particularly upset when he found out that his own salary was lower than that of several of the sales executives.

Together, Gray and the resident directors developed a system of grading which allowed three categories of monthly staff below the level of director. A salary scale was attached to each of these grades. Several anomalies still remained after this exercise, but the foundations of a more rational pay structure were laid. The redundancy which had just taken place gave the opportunity to grant fairly large rises to those whose pay had been particularly low for their responsibilities without coming into open conflict with stage three of the counter-inflation policy. The directors enjoyed working out the grading structures, and for several weeks Markland could be heard muttering 'graded managers make finer decisions'.

The final task was the reform of the pay structure for the clerical staff in grades covered by the clerks' union. Some time previously, a very complicated system had been agreed between this union and the company. It had no less than eight categories of weekly staff, and it was further complicated by merit and seniority payments. In addition, it had a productivity element related to the types of equipment which staff used. Gray, Lennon, and the junior work study officer set to work in an attempt to unravel the complexity of this system. For a week or so they were utterly defeated by this task. Eventually, the junior work study officer suggested that the bar chart technique employed in earlier work should be used again. Each employee was depicted by a bar on a long chart covering the eight categories. The result was astonishing. Six individuals were earning at least double that of others in their respective grades. These were found to be men who had been transferred in the past from clerical jobs on the shop floor to the offices. Gray suggested that these should be transferred back to shop floor jobs. Otherwise, he argued, the company might have to grant impossibly high salary increases under the equal pay legislation which was coming into operation. Markland gleefully acted on this suggestion and immediately arranged these transfers. The bar chart also showed that earnings were seriously out of line with pay rates. Many individuals in lower grades earned more than others who were one, two, or even more grades higher. The dip in earnings was particularly marked in the middle of the bar chart.

Gray, Lennon, and the junior work study officer rearranged individuals on a simpler—and what seemed to them—more rational scale of responsibility. They were concerned to rectify the grosser anomalies in pay, and wanted especially to pay higher rates to newcomers with the object of attracting better quality staff. Discussions with the clerks' union started, and Muldoon insisted that he should be involved, as many of the staff involved worked in his department. Markland agreed to this.

The prepared scheme had three basic grades with an additional low one for trainees and temporary staff and a high one for a few key workers. The union representatives were in broad agreement, but they wanted to alter the grades of a few specific jobs. At the end of the first meeting Gray and Lennon were quite confident that an agreement would be reached at the next meeting.

When he visited the factory on the Thursday of the following week he was incensed to learn that the meeting had already taken place and that Muldoon had agreed to three additional job grades. On the way to the boardroom for coffee he commented to Johnson:

'This is absurd. It's a bloody sight worse than when we started.'

The boardroom was full, Gray sat down and sullenly munched a piece of buttered toast. The low buzz of conversation was suddenly shattered when Muldoon entered. In a raised voice Gray addressed the newcomer:

'What the hell do you think you are playing at? Why have you buggered up every bloody thing I've tried to do ever since I came to this bloody place?'

For a second or two Muldoon stood motionless beside the coffee table; although he was used to Gray's linguistic style, the ferocity of the attack and the language used, stunned him. Eventually he said:

'David told me I could take over the negotiations. I'm satisfied with the new agreement, and so is the union. I don't see what you've got to complain about.'

'You can't see! What the hell do you think Stuart and I have been doing for the past month or two?'

He paused, glaring at Muldoon and waiting for an answer, but when Muldoon seemed about to speak, Gray shouted:

'We've been sorting out the mess in your department so that we can have a simple sensible pay structure. Now you've come along in your usual blundering way and wrecked everything we've done. You've just agreed to an even more complicated pay structure, and for what? Damn all. I'm bloody sure David didn't want you to do that.'

Muldoon's calm deserted him, and with loathing in his voice he said:

'You just don't understand anything about office work. At least Stuart doesn't pretend to. Most of the clerks work in my department. Don't you think I'm entitled to have a say in how they're paid?'

'It's a funny thing, but your bloody department has caused us more trouble than the whole of the rest of the bloody works put together. The shop floor won't put up with any nonsense, they'll walk out at the drop of a hat. Most of your department consists of bloody old women most of whom aren't even in the union. Stuart has spent hour upon hour talking to those two women shop stewards from your department. All they're concerned about is that they personally come out better than anyone else from the deal. They're obsessed by petty status differences—just like you.

'I'm sick and tired of listening to your pompous lectures. How many times have you told us how important merit payments are? I don't suppose that the rest of the board know that you've never given anyone a merit increase since you've been here. That about sums you up. You don't think anyone has any merit other than yourself, that's why you talk so much about it.'

Muldoon was, for once, reduced to silence and, after a pause, Gray continued in quieter tones:

'The trouble is that we're forced to start from scratch. You've just given them an increase for nothing at all. You know we've promised to give them something at the annual review. Because of you we'll

163

have to give them two increases instead of one. It's too bloody stupid for words.'

In the stunned silence Johnson glanced at Leyland who sat beside him, and when their eyes met they both found it hard to suppress their laughter. As they left Leyland said to his companion:

'You've got to hand it to George—he's a born diplomat.'

Markland's commitment declines

Markland began to spend less and less time at Tufted. He lived in a company house in York, but he spent more and more of his time at his flat in London. At first he would travel down to London on Friday evenings and return on Mondays on the morning pullman. Gradually he began to leave earlier and arrive later. He began to spend an increasing amount of time at Total's head office in London during the week itself. He sensed that his position at Tufted had become more insecure, and he tried to counter this by reaffirming his relationship with Clarke, the group marketing director who had originally recruited him into Total.

This behaviour became a source of criticism among many of the members of the operating board. Even when he was at Tufted he tended to withdraw from day-to-day management to an increasing extent. More and still more of his time there was devoted to his monthly reports to the chairman. He seemed to become almost a prisoner within his own office.

Only Gray could come and go more or less as he pleased. One day Gray said to him:

'Why don't you buy a house of your own just around the corner. That's what the directors want to see. They want some sign from you which establishes that you're committed to this place.'

'I think it's too late, George. The daggers are out. They're after me. You can be sure that sometime late on in the Autumn or next Spring I'll be back at head office. There's no need for you to worry, George. You'll still be coming here long after I've gone.'

'What do you mean—the daggers are out?'

Markland did not answer this but continued:

'It's beginning to worry me. I drank the best part of a bottle of Scotch on my own last night.'

'David, you know that's bad. Look, whatever is wrong here it's not worth getting yourself into that sort of state, surely?'

'You're right, George.'

There was a short silence which was eventually broken by Markland:

'Are you booked into the motel tonight?'

164

'Yes.'

'I'll get my secretary to cancel that. Drive me back to York this evening. You can book into an hotel just around the corner from my house. It does first class meals. I'll bring Jean along.'

Markland was, as usual, an hour or so late for dinner. He apologized and introduced his friend. The gloom that had earlier enveloped him so completely seemed to have disappeared. He spoke expansively about his career at Total and about the problems at Tufted. Eventually, he said:

'Howard and Jack don't seem quite so effective as they used to be. I can see that Jack is doing a good job in sorting out all the mess which Tenniswood has created, but it's Howard that I'm really worried about. He seems to have lost all his snap. He doesn't generate ideas any more. What's wrong with him?'

'I agree. He does seem to have gone into his shell, but I'm not sure it's fair to put all the blame on him.'

'What do you mean?'

'Well, it's all happened since he took charge of personnel and all that. He only has little fiddling things to do. He can run that outfit with his eyes closed. To be honest, he's hardly got a job to do. I think he's the sort of chap who needs a bit of a challenge. I've told you again and again what I think is the main problem at Tufted—production and sales just move in opposite directions. Howard is the only man in the place who might be able to do something about it, but he can't do anything until you make him marketing director. You just have to get rid of Palmer first. How do you think it looks from Howard's angle? He won't feel secure until he has a place on the board in his own right.'

'You're probably right, George.'

'I know I am.'

When Markland was about to depart with his friend he said:

'I'll leave you to pay the bill!'

Gray gulped visibly so he added:

'Don't be a fool, George. I'll sign your expenses in the morning.'

After they had left, Gray went to his room and began to undress. He caught a glance of himself in the mirror and said out aloud:

'Yes, he's right. You are a fool.'

He recalled, somewhat painfully, a conversation which he had had earlier that day with Lennon.

'George, why don't you fill up at the factory pump?'

'I don't think I'd better as I already claim the full mileage allowance. What do you think?'

Lennon looked blankly ahead, and then said:

'It's entirely up to you.'

'No, I think perhaps it's overdoing it a bit.'

He cursed inwardly to himself and thought: I'm wearing out my car doing work for Tufted. Next time I get that sort of offer I am going to accept.

Comings and goings

Gray saw less of the top brass of Total Furnishings than did Johnson and Leyland. Although he was by nature sceptical, he felt that what they, and others, had told him about group directors was embroidered to say the least. He had seen the immense figure of the chairman getting in and out of his chauffeur driven car. Even such brief glimpses, however, confirmed in his mind all that he had heard about the chairman's arrogance and unapproachability. He had, on one occasion, been introduced to Palmer senior, the deputy chairman. The contrast between him and the chairman was striking. The latter's ample frame was extended—many would say overextended—by years of good living and lack of exercise. His second in command was, by contrast, a person of diminutive stature who seemed to be diminished still further by cares and worries. Gray dismissed him immediately, as a nonentity. The way in which the directors at Tufted danced attendance on this non-entity seemed to him to be comical in the extreme.

Gray had met the group transport director and, as reported earlier, had had an altercation with him. In his estimation even Tenniswood seemed, in comparison, to be able. He was in for a greater shock. One day Markland called him into his office and said:

'George, what are you doing for lunch today?'

'Nothing, why do you ask?'

'Richard Woodcock is due to arrive at any minute. He's group director of economy. I don't think I can stand having lunch with him on my own. I don't ask many favours of you George, but just for once do me one. Join us for lunch in the boardroom.'

'Won't he expect to be taken out to some lush restaurant?'

'For God's sake, George, we'd never be able to get rid of him if we did that. The backing plant manager is going to take him around the factory this morning, but I've arranged for him to interrupt lunch so that he can take Woodcock to Cleckheaton. If everything goes according to plan you won't have to endure his company for much more than an hour.'

'He'll expect to be shown around by a director at least, surely?'

'Yes, but that's not possible! You see, the word got about and the place is completely deserted.'

Gray laughed out uncontrollably, and after recovering slightly said:

'I wondered what was happening this morning. The staff car park suddenly looked and sounded like Brands Hatch. I thought everyone had gone completely bonkers.'

'Yes, there's not a bloody director in the place and even Howard and Jack have joined the exodus.'

Markland grinned boyishly and continued:

'So you see, George, we've got to hold the fort together.'

Lunch itself fully lived up to expectations. Woodcock had driven up from his home in Rye, Sussex, the previous day and he recounted, in minute detail, each traffic delay and diversion. He reeled off road numbers—the M that and the A this—and he inflicted on his captive audience an account of the merits and shortcomings of the various restaurants *en route*. After a quarter of an hour or so of this he turned to Markland and asked:

'How are you doing here, David old chap? How is the jolly old export getting along, eh?'

The managing director quoted a few figures and the visitor started off again.

'Cracking good show, what? If everyone was pulling their weight like you then the country wouldn't be in the mess it is. Well done. Let's lick the Japanese at their own game. That's what I say. The grand old country is not finished yet you know. If it wasn't for the damn unions and the reds we'd do it easily. How's it going on the industrial relations front old man?'

Markland turned to Gray who contrived to maintain an attentive and interested posture, at least when Woodcock was looking in his direction.

'You are more in touch with industrial relations here than me, George, but I get the impression things are much quieter now.'

'Yes, David, we did have quite a few problems but they seem to have sorted themselves out quite well.'

This was quite sufficient to prompt Woodcock into another characteristic soliloquy.

'Pleased to hear it. You've done a good job there, young fellow. I wish there were more like you. All those professors and that in business schools sitting on their backsides all day. It's about time they got out into the real world and started putting their shoulders to the wheel. You don't mind if I give you a piece of advice do you?'

'No, of course not,' answered Gray.

'Don't be soft on the reds and trouble makers when you find them. There is nothing wrong with the good old British worker whatever they say. He's really honest at heart. The trouble is that he can be too

167

easily led astray. We're here to provide leadership. Just remember that.'

Without blushing Gray replied:

'Exactly my sentiments, Sir.'

After the backing plant manager had called to take the director of economy to Cleckheaton Markland remarked:

'I don't know about you, George, but I could use a drink right now.'

After he had opened the drinks cabinet Gray said:

'I would never have believed that top directors could be quite as stupid as that.'

Without the slightest hint of irony Markland replied:

'I'm not joking, George, but he's a lot brighter than most on the board at Total. When you meet that sort you begin to wonder what on earth you are doing.'

'Yes. I think I'm wasting my talents doing a non-job at the business school for a pittance. Perhaps there's something in the saying "you've got to be thick to get on in industry". I'm beginning to wonder whether we ought to use our intelligence so as to appear much more stupid than we really are.'

After another drink Markland told his companion:

'When I first came here I unthinkingly booked him into the motel. You'd never believe the fuss he created. He insisted on staying at the Silver Birches in Harrogate.'

'It must cost a bomb to stay there.'

'It does.'

The failure of a policy

The new product strategy, so eloquently proclaimed by Markland at the Middlesbrough conference, in the end came to nothing. Almost everyone at Tufted seemed to be too intent on preserving their departmentalized interests and on following established routines, for this policy to stand the slightest chance of success. On several occasions Gray suggested some ideas to the managing director about how this policy could have been implemented. He argued that a small study group consisting of Johnson, Leyland, and a management trainee should be formed. Its first task would be to list the sorts of carpet which were obvious loss makers. These would be withdrawn from the catalogue. The next task would be to pinpoint which of the remaining ranges caused disproportionate production problems. After this, it was proposed that the group should find out which were the slowest moving stocks in the warehouse. It seemed obvious that if a range of carpet fell within both of these categories then it too should be withdrawn.

Markland listened to suggestions of this kind patiently, but did not authorize any action along these lines. Toward the end of the quiet period he explained to a frustrated Gray:

'Your ideas are all right so far as they go, but my problems go deeper than you think. If we had control over our own marketing I'd have given the go-ahead to these ideas of yours long ago. I want the chairman to change my responsibilities here. Look, I'm responsible for Tufted as a profit centre, but I've got to make and sell what others decide, not what I want. That's contradictory.

'I've not told you this before, George. A month or so back I went to Holland. By chance I bumped into Birtwhistle. We're both getting on the plane to come home and who comes up the steps behind us—the group export director. On the plane I asked him why we don't sell more of Tufted's products in Totals' shops there. I'd found out that a lot of our stuff is distributed through other channels. It didn't make sense because the retail mark-up out there is terrific. He seemed to be very enthusiastic about what I was saying. I don't know why I didn't keep my trap shut. I don't think I am usually that naive; perhaps it was all that champagne I drank on the flight. Anyway, the next day I got a real rocket from the chairman. He has issued instructions that UK directors aren't allowed to go abroad on business without his permission.'

Gray let out an exclamation and Markland continued:

'What's the point in trying, George? I withdrew Cumberland Turf from the catalogue. We all know what a hopeless line that is. But what happened? By return post I get a letter from the group export director demanding more of the damn stuff. I'm giving up fast. Everywhere you go in this damn corporation you see notices; "private keep out".'

Later that day Markland took Gray into the factory and said:

'You see that great pile of rubbish over there? That's meant to be printed carpet. A while back Palmer mentioned at a board meeting that some company or other was doing great business in selling low-cost printed carpet. Of course, that did it. The chairman jumped at the idea and gave the go-ahead. Of course, there's no machinery here for printing and apparently there's no money either to buy any. So what do we do? We've been dispatching unbacked carpet to a firm in Aberdeen for printing. It's then returned here for backing. They've been having all sorts of problems commissioning their new plant. That pile is the result. It's all imperfect. We've been trying to fill in the badly printed sections by using "magic markers" which roughly match

169

the printed colours. That bloody great pile is just too bad to even attempt matching so we've got to send it all the way back to Aberdeen.'

Strained relations

Markland became even more irritable than usual as the quiet period drew to a close. Even Gray became very wary of him. The managing director seemed to be growing closer to Johnson, who accompanied him with increasing frequency on his visits to London.

One day Johnson and Gray were bemoaning the fact that the directors were wasting their time in drawing up ridiculous expenditure budgets for the next financial year when Markland entered the office. Gray greeted him in a friendly manner and cracked a joke. This prompted the managing director to erupt furiously:

'Haven't you got anything better to do than sit about playing the clown? I'm sick of you and your bloody idiocies. Get stuffed.'

He turned his back on the consultant and talked to Johnson about budgets. Gray found himself trembling with rage. He felt he was going to hit Markland, but some ingrained inhibition held him back at the last moment. Instead, he sat there silently and saw that Johnson was doing his best to pretend that nothing had happened.

On the way home in the train he felt ashamed of himself and thought:

'I should have hit the bugger instead of just taking it lying down. What right has he got to go around insulting everybody? Who the hell does he think he is?'

He knew that he had remained silent because to do otherwise would have cost him his consultancy. He realized that his silence had, for the moment, cost him his self-respect. The thought occurred to him that corruption had many faces. Fiddling expenses was a small matter compared to the act of sacrificing self-respect to gain money and favour.

By the time he was home he had resolved to answer back in future whatever the cost. With this resolve he felt better in himself, but from then on his relationship with Markland was never to be the same again.

16
The acceleration of events

Delayed action

Quite early in May, Markland announced that Johnson was to be appointed marketing manager. Privately he said to Johnson:

'It's just while I ease Palmer out of the organization—you are in charge of marketing from now on. You have full authority to make whatever changes are necessary. Palmer is marketing director in name only.'

Amazingly, he seemed to think that these private words gave Johnson an authority which would be recognized and respected by others. As he never informed Palmer, nor anyone else, of the authority which had been conferred on Johnson it was hardly surprising that they continued to regard Palmer as the operational as well as the titular head of marketing. Johnson was now at a complete loss; he could do nothing, but try to work with Palmer and tread water, until such time as Markland took action.

Privately, Gray told Markland that he thoroughly disapproved of this change, but his patron tried to explain that it was only a temporary expedient.

Belatedly, Markland decided to attempt to unseat Muldoon and Palmer. The situation regarding the former was complicated by the fact that he reported to Jones, the group financial director, as well as to Markland. This dual responsibility arose out of the fact that the management of funds was centralized at Total's head office. Markland telephoned Jones and arranged to have a meeting with him over lunch.

Wednesday 15 May—lunch with Jones

Jones arrived at the Leeds factory at 12.00. Early that morning Markland had discussed plans with Johnson. It was decided that Markland would raise the question of Muldoon early on at lunch and that Johnson should help to elaborate some of the more technical points concerning the system of management accounting.

At 12.30 p.m. the three of them set off in Johnson's car for a restaurant some seven miles away in the Dales. Markland sat beside

Johnson in the front, and throughout the journey he engaged Jones in small talk and company gossip. He did not mention Muldoon until they were at the bar waiting for their table to be made ready.

'I'm facing a minor revolt on the board. They're all complaining about the nature of the information we are getting from the system. I'm under a lot of pressure to do something about Muldoon.'

Jones replied without hesitation:

'What's basically wrong with the system? We've a similar one at St Albans, and that seems to operate effectively enough.'

Markland turned to Johnson and invited him to elaborate. Johnson chose his words carefully because he guessed that Jones must have agreed to bring in the consultants in the first place and had afterwards given his approval to their recommendations. He therefore concentrated his criticism on the way in which the system was operated rather than on its underlying assumptions. In this way he hoped that it would be clear to Jones that the difficulties were largely, or wholly, attributable to Muldoon.

Jones' reaction seemed favourable. He agreed that Muldoon should go, in principle, but he argued that this could not happen until after the end of the financial year. Like the chairman, he considered that his immediate removal would delay the presentation of financial statements.

Markland sensed that there was nothing more to be gained by pursuing the matter further so he changed the conversation to other topics.

Friday 31 May—A group meeting

The chairman held periodic meetings to discuss group problems with senior executives from head office and the subsidiaries. Included on the agenda of a meeting held on 31 May was an item relating to Tufted's sales. Markland, Palmer, Muldoon, and Johnson—the latter in his new role as marketing manager—were invited to attend.

The meeting was held in a luxurious boardroom at company headquarters. There was accommodation for about fifteen, but on that occasion the attendance was about twenty-five with the result that the room was uncomfortably crowded. Quite early on the chairman invited Markland to outline the current sales position. The latter explained that a general economic recession had combined with a severe slump in the building trade to depress carpet sales. He expressed his disappointment at the fact that sales over the last six months had fallen below budgeted targets, but he added that Tufted had nevertheless increased its share of a declining market. This, he pointed out, was a considerable achievement. The relative position of

Tufted within the group could, he argued, be improved if the distribution company were to absorb more stock. The chairman interrupted and said that this transfer would not be reflected in the group balance sheet and could not therefore serve any useful purpose. He went on to explain that it might be a good idea for overseas companies to take shipments early, and he stated that the Australian subsidiary would be an ideal candidate. The advantage of this expedient was that Tufted would be able to claim credits in respect of such shiploads from a government agency which helped to finance exports.

After a moment's pause the chairman rejected his own suggestion and made a public exhortation to Markland to 'pull out all stops' in the next month.

Just after eleven o'clock two glamorous secretaries entered the boardroom with coffee and plates of crustless cucumber sandwiches. One of the two secretaries, especially, caused some consternation among the executives from the subsidiaries. The delicate fabric of her blouse afforded an almost unimpeded view of her unsupported breasts which swayed gently as she moved. This spectacle had less novelty for head office executives whose enjoyment of it was consequently more discreet.

While refreshments were being taken the chairman suddenly stood up and announced that he and Palmer (senior) were leaving to have lunch with some Arabs. He commanded a managing director from one of the subsidiaries to take the chair in his absence, intimating that he would be returning some time in the afternoon.

Until the chairman returned at about 4.00 p.m. the proceedings assumed a rambling character as it was clearly understood by all present that it was unthinkable to attempt to resolve even the most minor issues in his absence. Johnson noted to himself that this pattern of behaviour was replicated in Tufted's boardroom when Markland absented himself.

When the formal meeting ended Markland and Johnson went to Clarke's office. Clarke was group marketing director. On Markland's behalf he had been taking informal soundings about how Palmer might be removed from Tufted. He said that he had drawn a complete blank and that no other subsidiary would accept him. He went on to suggest that Markland might be able to invent a 'special project' which would effectively remove Palmer from any executive role at Tufted while still retaining him on the payroll. Markland speculated on the possibility that he might be given a role as European salesman, but Clarke pointed out that such a move would almost certainly be blocked by the group export director. Johnson found this conversation very depressing as his further progress at Tufted now seemed to depend entirely on Palmer's removal.

Quite by accident, Johnson met Palmer in the dining car of the Leeds train. There was little outward personal antipathy between the two, but it was not difficult for Palmer to appreciate that Johnson had been transferred to his department with the express intention of easing him out. They both recognized this, but had never approached the subject even obliquely. Johnson was surprised when Palmer, quite suddenly, said that Markland was politically naive. He went on to recall the episode at Astwell Hall and stated that it was a bad error on Johnson's part to have supported Markland on that occasion. This, he suggested, had cost Johnson the support of a number of the directors at Tufted. He went on to explain that he had witnessed the departure of several previous managing directors of the subsidiary. It usually happened, he said, when the shape of the financial accounts became clear sometime in July or August. This period he called the 'chairman's silly season'.

Johnson knew that Palmer had had a difficult relationship with the chairman. At one time he had been a person of some power, but his influence had declined as a result of personal disagreements with the chairman. Johnson also, of course, knew something of the moves which had been made to unseat Palmer, and although these had not yet been successful he did not feel particularly threatened by these disclosures.

Thursday, 6 June—lunch with Smith
Smith and Johnson were alone together in the boardroom on the morning of the sixth of June. The other directors were either absent from the factory or had departed after taking coffee. Markland was in London.

'We ought to have a chat about things now that you're in marketing, Howard.'

Smith then suggested that they went out to lunch, and Johnson was pleased enough to accept this invitation. During lunch Smith looked at Johnson and said:

'The closure of the cutting room was the most disastrous thing this company has ever done. It has cost us a lot of sales, and unless we reverse that decision, we're finished.'

Johnson was somewhat taken aback by the directness of this remark. Smith rarely took an active part in policy discussions; normally his conversation was anecdotal. Quite automatically, Johnson repeated the standard arguments that had led to the closure and pointed out that the recent sales figures suggested that little, if anything, had been lost as a result. Smith listened in silence and then said:

'We broke faith with many customers. We've lost a lot of friends and we'll feel the pinch on orders very soon.'

It was unprecedented for Smith to have taken Johnson out for lunch, and it was unusual for him to take the initiative by introducing a business topic. These considerations might have alerted Johnson to the possibility that Smith was trying to warn him or give him a chance to redeem himself.

Monday 17 June—meeting with the chairman

Markland was regularly in contact with the chairman over the telephone but saw him much less often. In these conversations he had made some indirect references to Palmer, but the absence of face-to-face contact had had an inhibiting influence on him. Accordingly, he asked to have a meeting with the chairman. This was arranged for Monday 17 June at 3.30 p.m. in the Dorchester Hotel. It was agreed that the deputy chairman and Johnson should also be present.

Markland and Johnson arrived at the appointed hour and enquired at the desk. The chairman was well known to the hotel staff and they informed them that he was still in the restaurant. The two sat down in the lounge and waited. At four o'clock, the chairman emerged with his party into the foyer and went to the door to see them off. Markland and Johnson followed at a discreet distance and waited for him to be free. He acknowledged their presence with a nod, and they followed him into the lift and from there into his private suite.

Palmer (senior) and the chairman sat in armchairs on either side of the fireplace. Markland and Johnson sat on the couch. It was a curious feature of meetings with the chairman that nothing ever seemed to be the subject of a two-way discussion. He would launch into a monologue which he would occasionally punctuate to allow someone else to start to answer a question; they were never allowed to finish.

After a short while the chairman brought up the matter of Palmer (junior). Markland chose his words very carefully so as not to offend the latter's uncle. He did not criticize Palmer directly nor did he question his competence. However, he did suggest that his talents might be better employed in another part of the group. The chairman and his deputy concurred. After a few moments the chairman said:

'We will give serious consideration to this matter.'

Johnson had not participated in the meeting, except to make formal responses to polite enquiries about his health.

Wednesday 19 June—an appointment with the export director
The export sales director arranged a meeting at a large country house near St Albans so that executives from subsidiaries could be shown some 'sales presentation kits' which had been devised by an advertising agency. Johnson was to represent Tufted on this occasion.

On the Tuesday evening prior to the meeting, Johnson was working with Markland on budget targets for the next financial year. At about 9.00 p.m. Markland said:

'I think we've done enough for one day. I'll see you first thing in the morning.'

Johnson pointed out that he had to go to St Albans in the morning. Markland was unenthusiastic about this and suggested to him that, if it was not absolutely vital, he should not go.

First thing in the morning Johnson telephoned St Albans to make a formal apology to the executive who was in charge of conference arrangements. Somewhat to his surprise he found himself talking to the export director himself. In response to the formal apology the terse reply came back:

'Why can't you attend?'

'Mr Markland asked me to stay and help him with next year's budget.'

'Did he know that you had a meeting with *me*?'

The emphasis was clearly on the last word. Johnson apologized further and eventually was allowed to put down the receiver. The export director was a very powerful man; he was a confidant of the chairman and second only in importance to him. It was known that it was very dangerous to upset the sensibilities of this man, and although he had acted inadvertently, Johnson understandably felt more than a shade apprehensive.

Monday 1 July—an enquiry
The group's financial year ended on 30 June, and on the week-end of 29/30th stocktaking took place at Tufted. This was the apex of Muldoon's year and he was in his element. He started with his team first thing on Saturday morning. They continued well into the evening and recommenced early on the following morning. Muldoon himself worked throughout the night apart from taking about an hour's sleep on a camp bed that he had brought into work especially for the purpose.

At the end of each financial year the board had to approve the budgets for the next twelve months. This approval was, in effect, entirely synonomous with that of the chairman. For weeks past, Markland and the operating board at Tufted had been working frantically on budget preparation. The chairman was due at Tufted on 3 July to hear Markland present his marketing budget. The latter believed that the chairman's acceptance of this was vitally important to himself.

Unexpectedly, the chairman arrived with the deputy chairman and the export director just after lunch on Monday. At once they installed themselves in the boardroom. After a short while they summoned Markland and asked him to explain to them what seemed to be a contradiction in the stock figures which had just been circulated by Muldoon. Markland was stumped and he sent for Johnson so that the latter might explain the apparent inconsistency.

When Johnson arrived Markland repeated the chairman's question. A large quantity of carpet (about 100 000 square yards) was shown to have passed from the final stage of work-in-progress, but it failed to appear in stock. Johnson had long since abandoned all hope of finding useful information in the sheafs of paper periodically produced by Muldoon, but it seemed to him that the discrepancy could be easily accounted for if the carpet was awaiting final inspection before passing into the warehouse. The chairman did not want to accept this explanation and he asked for Muldoon to be summoned.

Muldoon's appearance was dramatic when he arrived at the boardroom. He had been at work for about 30 hours; he was dressed in old clothes made dirty from climbing over piles of carpet; he was, and looked, very tired. He presented a striking contrast to both Markland and Johnson, neither of whom had been involved in stocktaking. Muldoon was presented with the apparent anomaly and explained, as Johnson had, that the discrepancy was caused by an increase in stock awaiting final inspection. Markland and Johnson were both aware that this episode put them in an unfavourable light in the eyes of the chairman. Certainly, Muldoon could not have staged a more effective demonstration of how devoted he was to his work and to the company.

The chairman and his entourage left for an hotel in the country about 30 miles away where they always stayed when visiting Tufted. Muldoon went home, and Markland was left with Johnson to continue their work on budgets. They remained at this task until about 6.30 p.m. when Markland suggested that they should ring the chairman and ask if they might join him over dinner to discuss the budget. Markland was sensitive to the impression that had been made by Muldoon and felt that he needed to show that they too spent long hours in the service of the company.

His invitation was rejected by the export director who informed him that the chairman had already made arrangements for dinner.

Markland had earlier toyed with the idea of calling on the chairman unannounced at his hotel. If he had done so he would have found that the chairman's guests that evening were Palmer, Smith, and Muldoon.

Tuesday 2 July—a knock on the door

On the following afternoon Johnson and the product manager were working with Markland in his office on budgets when there was a peremptory knock on the door. The chairman's head appeared and he beckoned Markland into the adjoining room. Five minutes later Markland returned, ashen faced. He dismissed his colleagues and said:

'I've got something to think about.'

Johnson delayed his exit momentarily and asked what was wrong. Markland gave a weak smile and said:

'Nothing for you to worry about. I've just got a slight problem.'

Johnson returned to his office feeling uneasy. His misgivings were increased when he later saw Markland being driven through the factory gates by Clarke, the group marketing director.

At 11.30 p.m. Johnson's telephone rang getting him out of bed.

'It's happened,' said Markland on the other end of the line.

'Fired?', questioned Johnson.

'Good as, but you haven't heard the worst yet—Smith is the new managing director.'

Markland went on to tell him that during the brief time he was with the chairman, he had been told to reverse his production policy and re-establish the cutting room—or resign. The chairman had nominally offered him his old job back in group marketing, but in the same breath said that he assumed that Markland would not want that. Markland continued:

'I've got to give him an answer in the morning. I don't know about you and Jack. I think that I could ask the chairman to guarantee your jobs for six months or I could ask him to give you six months' pay in lieu of notice.'

Even later that night Gray was awakened by a call from Markland who said:

'Don't go to the factory on Friday.'

Gray was mystified and replied:

'Why? Lennon has especially asked me to be at a meeting with the shop stewards and a union official about manning levels on that day.'

Markland would not say why and kept on repeating the message not to go. Eventually, under further pressure for an explanation he said:

'I've been overtaken by events,' and promptly put the telephone down.

Wednesday 3 July—Markland resigns
Clarke, the group marketing director, and Markland were already in the office when Johnson arrived. Markland at once showed him a small hand written note addressed to the chairman which read: 'Due to the pressure of other commitments . . . I have no option but to resign.'

'What shall I do about you and Jack?' asked Markland.

Johnson had already made up his mind that it would be better to remain employed for the next six months rather than look for another job while on the dole. He did not answer because Clarke interjected:

'I see no evidence that Howard and Jack are in any danger. As far as I can see they will continue as though nothing had happened. I think that Howard is likely to be the next MD—after Smith's undoubted downfall next year.'

'A bit of a mixed blessing being MD of Tufted—don't you think?' said Johnson.

'Just because the previous MD's have stormed the hill and failed doesn't mean that you won't be the lucky one who storms the hill and wins.'

It was agreed that Markland would not mention anything about Howard and Jack. He kept his appointment with the chairman and handed over his letter of resignation. A grateful company gave him six months' salary as a leaving present and swiftly bade him goodbye.

Later that morning Clarke went to Johnson's office.

'I'm rather less optimistic now. I've just been with Smith and he's insisting that you and Jack go too.'

For the rest of the day the chairman and the directors were in session in the boardroom. Johnson and Leyland were not summoned. Later in the afternoon Gammage emerged from the boardroom in order to obtain some information from Leyland. The latter was with Johnson in his office. Gammage did not enter the office as was his custom. This normally mild and undemonstrative director symbolized a new relationship by tapping on the window, summoning Leyland by pointing at him, and then jerking the index finger of his right hand.

In the evening the backing plant manager from Cleckheaton had arranged a booze-up at a pub just outside the mill. Johnson was invited, and he met Palmer there. The latter told him:

'No decision has been reached on you and Jack, but if the worst comes to the worst they'll probably give you six months' notice. We've nothing against you both; George Gray is the bastard we can't stand.

When he comes here on Friday we'll have a reception committee waiting ready for him.'

On that evening Gray telephoned Lennon to find out what was happening. His friend told him:

'David's been fired. Howard and Jack are for the bullet as well. I think that's rather vicious; it's not necessary to get rid of them as well. Some of us objected, but Smith, who is the new MD, insisted that they went. It's a damn shame, I can't say how sorry I am, but there's nothing anyone can do about it now. Whatever you do, don't come to the factory on Friday. Palmer is organizing something very unpleasant if you do.'

Almost as an afterthought Lennon added:

'They've made Muldoon into a director and the sales manager has replaced Smith as sales director.'

In response to Gray's questions he explained that the official reason for Markland's dismissal was that he was devoting too much of his time to outside interests. Both men said goodbye and expressed the mutual hope that they would see each other in the not too distant future.

The next evening Gray received a further telephone call from Markland who apologized for his curtness earlier. He explained that he had had a basinful and did not feel like going into details at the time. Gray said that he understood and had in the meantime got the news from Lennon. Markland replied:

'I expected you to phone Stuart.'

Later that evening Gray's wife took a message from Johnson who also telephoned to explain what had happened and to warn his friend not to go to the factory.

Thursday 4 July—independence day

Early in the morning, well before either Johnson and Leyland were likely to arrive at work, Palmer went through their offices to clear them of everything except personal belongings.

Quite by coincidence, Johnson was moving that day to a house in a suburb of Leeds which he had just purchased on mortgage. Jack had agreed to take the morning off to help with removals. They returned to Tufted at about 3.00 p.m.

As they walked into the building the receptionist told Johnson that Smith wanted to see him immediately. Instead of obeying, they went to Johnson's office. At once they noticed that the room had been cleared and that Johnson's personal papers were in a neat pile on the top of the desk. The telephone rang as soon as they entered.

'Robert here,' said Smith, 'could you come and see me please.'

As Johnson entered, Smith looked up and motioned him to sit down. He pushed a letter towards him and said:

'I'm very sorry Howard, there's nothing I can do about it.'

A slightly less than grateful company was offering two months' salary as a leaving present. Smith demanded Johnson's car keys and said that he would arrange for him to be driven home. Johnson went back to his office where Leyland was waiting.

'It's only two months' pay Jack,' he said.

At that moment the telephone rang and Smith's voice said:

'Is Jack there?'

17
First order management

Masterson's resurrection

The chairman gave Markland's predecessor, Masterson, a modest golden handshake. Masterson was too young to retire, but too old to start on something entirely new. Although he had the best part of a lifetime's experience in the trade he found that other carpet manufacturers were not interested in offering him a job appropriate to his status. In their eyes his dismissal had cast a shadow of doubt over him; he was tinged with the stigma of failure. Masterson was a prudent man, but even with his leaving present his total resources were not great. Somehow, he had to find work. He decided that there was only one thing to do; he had to set up business on his own. This was for him a step into the unknown; he had always worked for others and never for himself. Circumstances made him much more consciously aware of his limitations than he had ever been before. He needed to have someone he could trust to help to take the step into the unknown. He was fortunate, indeed, to persuade the mill manager at Cleckheaton to join him as a partner in the new venture. This manager was an honest man with a fund of technical knowledge and much common sense.

They rented some premises in Huddersfield and with Masterson's capital acquired a modern tufting machine. Although they had to subcontract the work of backing to an established manufacturer they earned a very large profit in their first year. The amount they earned exceeded that which Tufted had made out of its twenty tufting machines and its other equipment in the same period. The resident directors were astonished by the magnitude and speed of the partners' success, and they often talked about it in the boardroom. Much later over a pint Lennon said to Johnson:

'If you multiplied their profit by twenty, the sum would be phenomenal. It sounds incredible, but there's no technical reason why Tufted couldn't do the same.'

The reason for the partnership's success was not all that difficult to fathom: it was a first order organization. The work of everyone there was essential. Masterson and his associate were not inactive bosses;

they could not afford to be. They acted as salesmen; they purchased raw materials; they supervised the work; when necessary, they lent a hand on the machine itself; they acted as maintenance engineers; they made up the pay packets, and they even made the tea. They did this and much more besides. In the best first order manner they turned their hands to any job which needed doing. They did not stand on their dignity and pretend that certain tasks were below them. They did not avoid work through delegation and appointment. They were not encased in ritualized ceremonies of the kind which absorbed the time of resident directors at Tufted. They had become first order managers; not from choice but from necessity.

A first order Tufted?

Could one imagine an organization, which was more than twenty times larger than the partnership, being run on first order principles? The writers believe that the answer is emphatically—yes. In fact, such organizations were the rule rather than the exception at the time when Britain was the foremost industrial nation.

Any organization which manages to perform its primary task, however inefficiently, must have within itself a sub-structure of first order activity. It just would not be able to work at all if this were not the case. If Tufted were stripped of its second, third, and fourth orders of administration the nature of this first order sub-structure would be open to inspection. Gray, Johnson, and Leyland saw this dimly through the glass. Shortly after the redundancy, the consultant remarked to Markland:

'You know, the cutting room closure put us on the wrong scent. We didn't need any excuses to close down the staff departments. It's a pity we stopped half way.'

'Heaven help us, George. The way you'd want it, I'd have no bloody managers under me at all. They're pretty thin on the ground as it is.'

He turned to Gray and a look of dismay came over his face as he contemplated the factory so denuded of staff and managers.

The consultant could not resist laughing at the managing director's discomfiture and said:

'Don't be silly, David. It would be excellent if Muldoon's department and Palmer's outfit were closed down.'

He chuckled again as Markland gave a weak smile, and repeated the words:

'Excellent, really excellent,' as he rubbed his hands together vigorously.

In fact, the reduction in staff had been quite substantial and it in no way adversely affected the performance of the factories or the sales force. Indeed, three weeks after the redundancy the factories achieved a record level of production. The long-term saving in administration overheads which resulted from the redundancy gave the company a breathing space and an opportunity to take stock.

It was relatively easy for Masterson and his partner to construct a lean first order company starting from scratch. An upheaval, even more savage than that which did occur at Tufted, would have been necessary to convert that organization into a lean first order company.

So many of the operational problems which beset that company were created or made worse by the existence of the higher orders of administration. In their day-to-day operations companies are largely self co-ordinating. It is totally fallacious to believe that they are co-ordinated through second and third order 'support systems'. Tufted achieved a degree of cohesion not because of the formal control and information systems which existed there, but rather in spite of them. The place continued to function because of the virtues of the much maligned sub-structure of first order activity which still somehow managed to survive. This sub-structure is typified in a remark which Lennon once made to Gray:

'You surely don't imagine that I get my information about stocks and materials from the production control office, do you? Whenever I want to know anything about them I go and see Mrs Briggs in the stores. She's the only person who's got a clue about what we've got and what we haven't.'

The existence of the staff departments actually served as a buffer beween senior management and the realities of the first order. Markland's dismay was due to his realization that their disbandment would leave nothing at all between himself and the concrete realities of the first order. This situation would expose those who lived in the world of administrative abstraction for what they were. It would be a situation in which the confusion which existed in Markland's mind between words and action would become plain for all to see.

Inevitably, most people are going to ingratiate themselves to some extent in the face of authority. The mechanisms of ingratiation were described in the chapter on Markland's dilemma. A first order organization cannot change human nature, but it does not offer such a fertile field in which to practise the art of ingratiation. After all, in it people are paid to perform essential operational tasks, whereas this was not the case in the staff departments at Tufted.

The writers believe that the deceptions, intrigues, and manipulations described, particularly towards the end of this book, were not entirely chance happenings. In their opinion, these unsavoury activities were stimulated by the very nature of the higher orders of administration.

The interplay of the four orders
In a first order organization people are paid for performing work which is essential to the accomplishment of the primary task. In such an organization patronage serves operational ends. With the development of the higher orders of administration, patronage becomes increasingly dissociated from operational requirements. At Tufted and Total, operational requirements were, in fact, subordinated to the needs of the patronage system. This outcome was not accidental; it arose out of the very nature of the higher orders.

On what is the growth of the higher orders of administration based? There has been, for a long time, a tendency for production methods to become more and more capital intensive. At the same time technical progress causes the efficiency of capital equipment to increase. The result is that it requires fewer and fewer men to produce more and more goods. This process was observable at Tufted and there was plenty of scope to carry it much further. For instance, given the necessary funds, the company could have replaced its older machines with newer, much more efficient ones. The latter would have enabled the company to obtain much higher outputs from a given amount of factory space. It would have been possible for them to have closed the mills at Cleckheaton and Batley. After certain changes in layout and some extensions had been made to the Leeds factory, the company would have been able, as a result of the new machinery, to produce more from this one factory than it previously did from all three. At the same time the amount of direct labour required would have been substantially reduced. Developments of this kind generate incomes which are much greater than those needed to pay first order personnel. Such economic surpluses can enable a company to introduce or extend the higher orders of administration.

The size of these surpluses can be very great indeed. Many companies can, as a result, afford to indulge themselves in spectacular status expenditures and continue to support extensive higher order administrations at the same time. Large ultra-modern offices on expensive city centre sites can often be easily afforded. Again, the costly furnishings and the jungles of exotic plants which these buildings often contain are further testimony to corporate wealth. Expensive computers not only serve to absorb surplus funds but also help to confirm the impression that management is a highly scientific calling.

Particular ingenuity was shown by one British food company. It constructed new offices built around two courtyards. One was filled with a flock of penguins and the other flamingoes. The moat around the building contained shoals of ornamental carp, and the whole was neatly rounded off by an enclosure at the bottom of the main stair-well which contained alligators. Such a solution to the problem created by economic surplus showed much more imagination than the purchase of a relatively mundane item such as an IBM 370—besides, this company already had one!

It must not be thought for one moment that expenditures of this kind usually represent conscious decisions to waste money. The perverse rationality of higher order administrators is such that they have no difficulty in persuading themselves that such expenditures can be justified on strictly economic criteria. The central city office advertises the success of the corporation and this image generates further success. Luxurious offices and their imaginative settings serve to make the work environment more attractive and comfortable. This raises morale, and office productivity benefits accordingly. Again, the executive jet saves valuable time and thus helps a company to use scarce managerial talent more effectively.

Companies are persuaded by these arguments, because other ways of disposing of surplus seem, by comparison, very unattractive. For instance, the surplus could be given to shareholders or passed on to consumers in the form of lower prices.

The expansion of the higher orders of administration fulfils the function of surplus absorption. As has been seen, the declared aim of the higher orders is to improve the performance of primary tasks. There is a built-in conflict between the purpose and the function of the higher orders. Both observation and logic suggest that the function must triumph over purpose. If the higher orders succeeded in fulfilling their purpose, to the extent that they made a net contribution, they would be unable to discharge their function of surplus absorption.

Unfortunately, the expansion of the higher orders is not confined to those companies which have requisite surpluses. The number and variety of higher order administrators which a company employ serve as an unmistakable outward symbol of its commercial success. The paradox of the higher orders is that they see themselves not as dependent on first order operations; rather they see themselves sustainers of these operations. In other words, they mistake effect for cause. This way of thinking is very prevalent. Firms which are not in a position to afford higher order administrators often recruit them in the belief that they are responsible for the commercial success of outstanding companies. Total was one of those unfortunate companies which fell into this trap. Markland was one of many higher order administrators which the company recruited in order to revitalize its management so as to lay the foundations of commercial success. Needless to say, this policy did not promote the desired results. In fact, a couple of years or so after the events described in the previous chapter took place, the company went into liquidation.

Once departments of second and third order administration are formed they tend to be propelled along by their own internal logic, even when the required economic surplus is lacking. This does not only happen to companies; it can even happen to nations as a whole. Britain, for instance, has experienced a phenomenal growth in the higher orders of administration within its public sector. One of the major political problems in this country is that it is becoming increasingly difficult to defray the cost of this administrative monster out of the resources of the public purse. A clear case of the parasite outgrowing the host on which it feeds.

Nations make the same mistake as companies; they confuse what J. K. Galbraith called 'symbolic modernization' with economic development. This consists of such things as a glittering airport, impressive state buildings, an army of officials and civil servants, and so on. Such symbolic modernization often takes place against a background of grinding poverty. It is ironical that a country like Nigeria provides, at the moment, a profitable market for management consultants and for those devoted to development of the higher orders of administration.

The road to corruption and decadence

The growth of the higher orders carries with it the seeds of deception, self-deception, inefficiency, and more ominously, corruption. The whole rationale of the second and third orders is based on a deception—an escape from empirical realities. In the abstract world of the higher order administrator all sorts of illusions are nurtured. Trained incapacity becomes synonymous with competence. People start calling things by their wrong names. Idleness and pretence are mistaken for hard work. Whole worlds of non-jobs and pretend work are created. This world saps energy and erodes integrity.

Those who live in the world of abstractions become dehumanized by the bureaucracies which are its outward manifestation. The collective brutality which possessed the operating board at Tufted during the time of the redundancy perfectly illustrated this dehumanizing influence.

In the chapter on the four orders it was shown how overmanning and overstaffing in the first order can contribute to the growth of the second and third orders. The existence of the intermediate orders is also stimulated by the desire of the fourth order to relieve itself of work.

The second and third orders hide the decadence of the fourth. They help to sustain the fantasy that management is meritocratic, scientific, and objective. Above all else, they conceal ambition and the abuse of power under their veneer of respectability.

Printed and bound by
Hazell Watson & Viney Ltd
Aylesbury
Bucks